The Story so Far

The Story so Far

Memories & Other Fictions

ERIC AMBLER

Weidenfeld & Nicolson
LONDON

The stories in this collection are previously published as follows:

'The Army of the Shadows' appeared in *The Queen's Book of the Red Cross*. London: Hodder & Stoughton, Ltd., 1939.

The stories in 'The Intrusions of Dr Czissar' appeared in various issues of *The Sketch* (London) 1940.

'The Blood Bargain' appeared in *Winter's Crime* 2. London: Macmillan, Ltd., 1972.

'The One Who Did for Blagden Cole' first appeared in *The Man Who*, edited by H.R.F. Keating, for the Detection Club. London: Macmillan, Ltd., 1992.

First published in Great Britain in 1993 by
Weidenfeld & Nicolson
The Orion Publishing Group, Orion House
5 Upper Saint Martin's Lane
London WC2H 9EA

British Library Cataloguing in Publication Data
is available

ISBN 0 297 84048 7

Typeset by The Spartan Press Ltd.,
Lymington, Hants.

Printed by Butler & Tanner Ltd.,
Frome, Somerset.

Contents

Foreword

Second Thoughts on an Epitaph

SOME years ago, when I was living in Switzerland, George Weidenfeld wrote suggesting that I should do an autobiography. He had just had a great success with such a book written by another of his authors, a playwright. I had been a screenwriter in Hollywood as well as writing a number of successful thrillers. Would I give the suggestion serious thought.

I did give it thought. I had brought myself up to believe that novelists should be read but rarely seen and only occasionally heard. They write fiction and that is where the difficulty lies. It is the same for the popular genre novelist as for his betters in the serious set. The novelist's readers are often spoken of figuratively as if they were an audience. They are not; the novelist has an audience of one; one person in a collusive relationship with the author through the pages of a book. An autobiography calls for a sudden change in the relationship, and a different kind of attention. It is as if the waiter has suddenly pulled up a chair and become the host. The author, it seems, has things to say about his life and times that cannot better and more engagingly be said through fictional characters. Readers don't like that; they like the novels you write, not you. Readers like to know where they stand with a writer: is he a storytelling actor, an entertainer, or is he appearing on the stage as himself? Unless he has a life apart from his writing – a life of some sort of derring-do with plenty of names to drop – a popular novelist should keep himself to himself. Autobiography should be left to show-business characters, aging reprobates with beans to spill and the politicos.

When, eventually, a meeting in London was arranged at which the proposed autobiography would be discussed, I went to it with my mind made up. I was contracted to George for another novel. In due course he would get it.

I found, though, that I was not dealing with George alone. With him at the meeting was John Gross, lately editor of the *Times Literary Supplement*, a journal for which I have always had a profound respect. My objections to doing an autobiography came out more or less as rehearsed, but sounded to me now more peevish and defensive than thought through and sensible. It was Gross who answered them. It had been upon his advice that George had suggested an autobiography. *The Mask of Dimitrios*, he went on, was a bench-mark book that had changed the thriller form for good. It was, in its way, a famous book. Readers on both sides of the Atlantic would be interested to learn how its author came to write it. Was that so surprising? And had I not worked for ten years in Hollywood? Had I nothing of interest to say about that experience?

I should have tried answering that last question first. No, nothing of interest I should have said. All the word Hollywood reminded me of by then was the year of my life wasted trying to rewrite history to accommodate the jejune fantasies of Marlon Brando. Instead, I heard only the flattery. I was used to thesis-writing academic gush about my early work but from a former *TLS* editor a measured compliment like that was warming. I should have temporized, promised to think again. Instead, I said weakly that, of course, I would do my best to do the book.

The extent of my folly was not immediately apparent. I found a way of starting the book so that it read almost like a thriller; that was easy, but then I found myself having to describe my childhood and the rot set in; rot in all senses of the word. I began again. Diogenes, my German language publishers, had done a *festbuch* for my seventieth birthday and illustrated it with old family photographs provided by my sister. I had written captions for them and German readers had found the captions entertaining; there had been a light-hearted touch about them. A touch of some such kind was now badly needed. I scrapped everything and went back to the beginning.

There were more false starts. I ploughed on, writing and rewriting, deleting and abridging, expanding and contracting; I hated the thing; had it been a novel I would have discarded it as unworkable. As the book was supposed to be an attempt to explain myself there could be two valid reasons for my abandoning the attempt: either the true explanation was too banal for words, or the task of giving it was beyond me. Since I was unwilling to accept either of those propositions I felt obliged to continue. The difficulties of doing so were, no doubt, salutary; they compelled me to think as dispassionately as I could about my limitations as a writer and about the processes at work in a storyteller's development; but I don't think I succeeded in explaining myself. At what should have been the half-way point in the book, the point at which I should have described briefly and sensibly the break-up of my first marriage, I brought the book to an end. I had had enough of myself.

Here Lies was sympathetically received and enjoyed a modest success. Some liked the ambiguity of the title; others, though, were puzzled by the suggestion that the book was an epitaph, a last word, when its contents – in particular the absence of any account of the Hollywood years – suggested a second volume to follow.

At first I simply denied the second volume, saying with some feeling that I had had too much autobiography and wanted no more, of my own or anyone else's. I was not believed. My account of Hollywood could not be the usual visiting Britisher's hard-luck story. I had lived and worked there for ten years.

It was true that I had more to say about the writer's relationship with the film makers, but Hollywood had only a small place in it. What I had been thinking over was a book about screenwriting modelled on C.E. Montague's *A Writer's Notes on his Trade*. John Gross would have understood that notion, but he had moved on. When Peter Lewis, who was writing a critical study of my work for an American publisher, asked me about work in progress I could not deny that it had autobiographical elements or pretend that I was back to fiction again. The second volume of *Here Lies* was beginning to have a life of its own. When I telephoned Julian Symons the other day to ask him who, forty years ago, had proposed me for The Detection Club he asked me why it mattered. I tried to explain this book. 'Aha!' he said; 'the second volume at last.'

That it is not. It is a collection of nine short stories, all written during the last sixty years. Hardly a life's work, and some of them haven't worn very well, but collectively they suggest a narrative pattern that I have always found satisfying; that of a Beginning, a Middle and an End.

These stories belong to the places and the times and the circumstances in which they were written. So, instead of trying to repair their deficiencies, I have described the circumstances of the three periods of my working life of which they seem to be parts. If, somewhere in the Middle bit the word Hollywood occurs it refers not only to a suburb of Los Angeles but also to a state of mind that once existed there. That was in the days of black-and-white film, the major studios, the wicked old star system and the writing and directing talent drawn there from Central Europe; all long before the coming of satellite television.

Beginning

WHEN I began earning my living as a writer I did so in the copy department of an advertising agency. Other genre novelists of the period seem to have done the same thing. In the awful recession years of the early thirties a young scribbler with a lively mind could earn more in advertising than he could on the slow promotion ladders of even the liveliest provincial news-papers, and he would much sooner be able to see sentences that he himself had written in print on a published page.

Of course, advertising was in those days considered by serious persons to be a fairly disreputable occupation; novels like H.G. Wells' *Tono Bungay* and Rose Macaulay's *Potterism* had seen to that. Its present respectability, with advertising and PR persons to be found among the other semi-secret servants – speech-writers and the like – who steady the hands of those who steer the ship of state, has all the airs to be expected of the successful corner-boy. The boy's father, the one I knew, may have had sharper suits but his smile was rather more engaging. I was reminded of him recently when I was asked by an old friend whether it was true that in the thirties the copy departments of the big London advertising agencies were hotbeds of communism.

I thought that he must be joking and laughed; but he meant it and began rattling off lists: the Cambridge Marxists, the Oxford Pacifists, Harry Pollitt, John Strachey and the first Left Book Club titles. I remembered then that he was a few years younger than me and unfamiliar with the nether world in which I and most other big agency copywriters had worked. I had to remind him about the National Government of Ramsay MacDonald and the Tyneside hunger marchers, about the fear of losing one's job, any job, and of not having a shilling for the gas meter.

In advertising at the time, of course, we did not speak of such things. Our economic safety lay in optimism, bigger press advertising budgets, growth. We just looked at the ads in the morning papers; but we read the *Evening Standard*. There, David Low made fun of the politicians, Arnold Bennett reviewed books and W.R. Inge, the Dean of St Paul's, admonished practically everyone. True, most of us led double lives; that is to say we tried to make second careers for ourselves outside advertising; but I can think of none of us who dabbled in party politics. Of course, these notional second careers were hedges against possible unemployment but they were something more as well. We did not entirely despise our work. Indeed, in the invention and development of a successful campaign to increase the market share of, say, a brand-name baby food there could be a certain satisfaction. If it was the kind of satisfaction a trial lawyer is said to experience when he secures the acquittal of a well-heeled crook, what of it? Our reply to the objecting moralists would have been the same as his. We were hired hands lawfully employed. We were technicians of an artsy-crafty sort, like lawyers or character actors.

Not all of us wanted to write popular novels. In my first copy department there were one or two eccentrics. I was one – I wanted to write avant garde plays like Ernst Toller – another was an apprentice faith healer who was learning the mysteries of the art by working evenings as an assistant to a full-time healer, a woman with a busy practice in the Holland Park area. I have forgotten the man's name. Of those with literary ambitions Robin Fedden seemed at first the most likely to succeed, but later on he became an architectural historian. Cecil Maiden was our first published novelist and he also wrote short stories for shiny-paper magazines. He was a keen Christian Scientist and devoted to the music of Rutland Boughton. Much of a weekend with Maiden and his wife was spent listening to gramophone recordings of 'The Immortal Hour', a depressing work. The agency we worked in was the European off-shoot of an American agency with roots in Chicago and most of our bigger clients were of American origin. We were constantly made aware of trends in American popular taste and were quick to spot and sometimes anticipate their arrival here. One of us,

Gerald Butler, marked the arrival of the hardboiled sex-and-sadism crime story with a novel entitled *Kiss the Blood Off My Hands*. The title was a mite more entertaining than the book; Butler had a gift for phrase-making. We had a client who manufactured foundation garments and spent a lot of money advertising in the fashion magazines. With a few artfully chosen words Butler could make a rubber roll-on suspender belt sound like Coco Chanel's own personal underwear. The oldest among us was Philip Taylor who was in his forties, a shell-shocked survivor of one of the Somme battles with a violent temper and an appalling stammer. I shared an office with him for nearly a year and most of our conversations were conducted by scribbling what we had to say in the margins of newspapers. It was easier for him than endless stammering and I picked up the habit. Once, when in my haste to scrawl a reply I broke the point of the pencil, he seized the paper from me and wrote 'no need to shout'. Then, to my relief, he laughed. We got on well because we never met outside the office and never discussed anything except the theatre. He was a secret lyricist who wrote 'point' numbers and blue patter for nightclub entertainers. His work in advertising was better paid. He was an anarchist perhaps, but not a communist. We had no literary names in that agency. The nearest was Dorothy L. Sayers who worked in the copy department of one of our competitors a few streets away. Her improbable amateur detective Lord Peter Wimsey was already widely known in the better lending libraries.

It was Maiden who suggested that I should write short stories instead of rather depressing plays about failed suicides. Unknown playwrights were having a bad time anyway. The short story market, on the other hand, was booming. And by writing short stories I would in due course learn how to write novels.

I knew enough to know that this last suggestion was untrue. The short story was a form on its own, not a preparation for bigger things. I had not tried writing a short story because I saw only the difficulties it presented. In a one-act play I could overcome them. But if you tried explaining that sort of difficulty to Maiden you soon found yourself up against Mary Baker Eddy and walls of cotton wool. Besides, Maiden was a published author with hard covers to prove it so I took his advice.

What he advised, in effect, was a standard procedure in the copy department. When you were given the job of writing advertisements for a client for whom you had not written before you went first to the 'guard' books, or had them brought to you. These were the massive scrap books in which were kept complete records of all a client's previous campaigns. You saw what your predecessors on the account had done; you then tried to do something slightly, but not too radically, different. This time, however, it wasn't guard books I wanted from the department that kept them but voucher copies of the popular short-story magazines and pulp periodicals. I was given more than I could carry.

That was the heyday of periodical publishers like the Amalgamated Press. An attempt forty years later to catalogue the AP output in the thirties identified thirty-two separate weeklies selling for a few pence each; this was without counting the paper-bound serials. There were scarcely any crime stories. The dominant theme was Cinderella, but with some differences. Prince Charming tended to have a white-collar or white-coat job; Cinders was a charge hand on a factory floor or in a typing pool and the ugly sisters were personified by a selfish widowed parent who suffered from lower back pain and was a secret drinker. The good fairy could be anyone from a jobbing gardener to the orchestra leader at the local palais de danse.

I did not enjoy wading through this rubbish and I should have abandoned the idea of trying to reproduce it. The skills of a good copywriter were his abilities to say much in little and to say it lucidly; to say it with wit or in a particular style was not necessarily useful. In any case, such skills are not always transferable. But I was caught by the challenge.

I wrote three stories in what I believed to be the manner of the *Home Companion* romance and managed to tell myself that they were pretty good. Maiden thought they were pretty good, too, and decided that he would send them to his literary agent. She would undoubtedly sell the stories for me.

I was encouraged. Maiden's agent was a senior member of one of the better-known literary agencies of the period. She said she would see me. I can't remember the woman's name; I spent many years trying to forget it and seem at last to have succeeded. There were two literary agencies with offices at the Fleet Street end of the Strand. My appointment was in the smaller of the two. I went to keep it with a light heart.

She was a handsome woman with neatly bobbed hair and long earrings. She smiled at me in a kindly way as I sat down facing her. Then she picked up my three stories from the desk in front of her and dropped them again as if to see if they would bounce. When they didn't she gave me a thinner smile.

'Trash I expect you call it,' she said. 'Well, that's as may be. What it isn't is publishable trash. You make a mistake you clever young men. You think you can write down to the market. You think it's easy to write trash. You're wrong. It's easy to write imitation trash. It's quite difficult to write the real thing. For that you have to have a knack and, I'm afraid, a certain talent. On the evidence of these stories all you have is the trick of parody. Perhaps you agree, eh?'

'I was wondering why you bothered to see me.'

'I was coming to that. You don't really want to write stories do you?'

'No, not really.' Lying seemed easy by then.

'Good, I didn't think so. Have you met Cecil Maiden's wife?'

'Yes, I have. They asked me for a weekend.'

'Pretty woman. But she's too indulgent. The trouble is that Cecil gets these crushes on good-looking young men and tries to persuade them that they have writing talent.' It was all said with the sweetest of smiles. 'The Edwardians used to call it literary seduction I believe. I don't know what it's called now. Perhaps you can think of something.' She stopped smiling and held up the three typescripts. 'Do you want these back?'

'No thank you.'

She dropped them in the waste-basket by her desk. 'It was good of you to call. Tell Cecil I thought you showed great promise. He'll understand.'

But I was already at the door and on my way out. When I was back in the street again I tried for a moment to be sick, then went into a Lyons and had a cup of tea. It was years before I could pass that bit of the Strand without my toes curling at the memory. In the tea-shop I vowed never again to write a short story.

Instead I wrote an anachronistic thriller about a small state in Eastern Europe that succeeds in making an atomic bomb. It was published in 1936. That was the year the Spanish Civil War began, the year that started many of us, even copywriters in advertising agencies, thinking about the nature of a war to come. Suddenly I found myself with something to write about. By the summer of 1939 I had written five thrillers and was living comfortably in Paris. My fifth book was *The Mask of Dimitrios* and it was to be published in London as a *Daily Mail* Book-of-the-Month.

The month in question, however, was August '39, not a good month for books, nor indeed for much else in Europe. In those days the only Harry's Bar of any note outside Italy was the one in Paris. It was on the rue Blanche just down the hill from Bricktop's, the other friendly night-spot within easy walking distance of the Pigalle Metro. My companion in both places was Louise Crombie, fashion artist, born in Portland, Oregon, divorced and working in Paris to support a young family back in New Jersey. On the night of the twenty-second we were drinking brandy and soda and trying to decide whether to face the complications of an Anglo-American marriage under French law or to go on living together without legal or clerical blessings. There was going to be a war, but what sort of war? Who were going to be the allies against Hitler?

It was to Harry's Bar that night we went in search of news. There, just after midnight, a man used to come by selling early editions of the morning papers. So, that night, that was how we heard the awful news of the signing of the Molotov–von Ribbentrop non-aggression pact between the Soviet Union and Nazi Germany.

I can still recall the shock of that moment, and the pang of fear that came with it. I was a man of the Popular Front, that short-lived coalition of the European Left against the spread of Axis Fascism that was jumping the frontiers of Versailles Treaty Europe with the remorseless ease of a medieval plague. I believed, with many others, that the Munich Agreement of the year before had been a humiliating disaster, but I had also believed, also with others, that the Soviet Union would in the end join with the French and British democracies to confront and contain the common enemy. Now, suddenly, there was light on the stage and the hero could be seen climbing into bed with the villain. We did not know then, of course, that the pact signed by Molotov and Ribbentrop had, as well as giving the Nazis a free hand to take anything they wanted of the pre-1914 German territories, secretly partitioned Poland and ceded the Baltic States of Lithuania, Latvia and Estonia to the Soviet Union; but the fact that Stalin and Hitler had done a deal of any sort was enough. The war, for long inevitable, would now certainly be total.

A few days later we went to London. Our plan was to get married as soon as British law allowed. Louise would then have dual nationality and, if she wanted them, two passports. But several weeks would elapse before the marriage could take place. It was time to think about fighting the war. I was thirty then and if I waited to be called up with my age group I would end up in the army somewhere near the blunt end. Best to volunteer, I thought, and decided to consult a friend who, I was sure, would have contacts in high places. He had indeed, and soon got my name onto a priority list of volunteers for the Navy. All I had to do then was what everyone else on those lists was doing – wait for orders to report for an interview. Everyone, it seemed, was waiting for orders.

Everyone except my publishers, that is. They had orders from the City of London to compile and produce with all speed a celebratory book. It would be for sale throughout the British Empire and its purpose would be to raise money quickly for the Red Cross. The result was *The Queen's Book of the Red Cross*, a small-quarto volume of three hundred pages or so with a facsimile message from Her Majesty on Buckingham Palace paper and contributions from fifty authors and artists. It was an expensive book, with colour litho and photogravure illustrations to supplement the letter press text and a fine cloth board binding. Among the authors who contributed stories were Hugh Walpole, Daphne du Maurier and A. A. Milne; among the poets were T.S. Eliot and John Masefield; the artists included Laura Knight, Rex Whistler and Mabel Lucie Atwell. The most remarkable thing about it, however, was the speed with which the work was done. The whole process from editorial start to finished copies from the binders was accomplished in two months. The dogs of war can start some unusual runners.

The story I contributed, old resolutions forgotten, was *The Army of the Shadows*. I wrote it steadily, cutting and revising as I went as usual, but I wrote with few of the usual hesitations. I had something to say that would soon, I knew, become more difficult to say aloud or plainly: that our enemy was not the German People but the Nazi tyranny to which too many of them had submitted. Where better to say it than in a book that was going forth with a royal blessing?

The Army of the Shadows

I⊤ is three years since Llewellyn removed my appendix; but we still meet occasionally. I am dimly related to his wife: that, at least, is the pretext for the acquaintanceship.

The truth is that, during my convalescence, we happened to discover that we both like the same musicians. Before the war we usually met when there was some Sibelius being played and went to hear it together. I was a little puzzled when, about three weeks ago, he telephoned with the suggestion that I should dine at his house that night. There was not, I knew, a concert of any sort in London. I agreed, however, to grope my way through the black-out to Wimpole Street shortly before eight o'clock.

It was not until he had presented me with a brandy that I found out why I had been invited to dinner.

'Do you remember,' he said suddenly, 'that I spent a week or so in Belgrade last year? I missed Beecham doing the Second through it. There was one of those international medical bun fights being held there, and I went to represent the Association. My German is fairly good, you know. I motored. Can't stick trains. Anyway, on the way back a very funny thing happened to me. Did I ever tell you about it?'

'I don't think so.'

'I thought not. Well' – he laughed self-consciously – 'it was so funny, now there's a war on, that I've been amusing myself by writing the whole thing down. I wondered whether you'd be good enough to cast a professional eye over it for me. I've tried' – he laughed again – 'to make a really literary job of it. Like a story, you know.'

His hand had been out of sight behind the arm of his chair, but now it emerged from hiding holding a wad of typewritten sheets.

11

'It's typed,' he said, planking it down on my knees. And then, with a theatrical glance at his watch, 'Good Lord, it's ten. There's a telephone call I must make. Excuse me for a minute or two, will you?'

He was out of the room before I could open my mouth to reply. I was left alone with the manuscript.

I picked it up. It was entitled A Strange Encounter. *With a sigh, I turned over the title page and began, rather irritably, to read:*

The Stelvio Pass is snowed up in winter, and towards the end of November most sensible men driving to Paris from Belgrade or beyond take the long way round via Milan rather than risk being stopped by an early fall of snow. But I was in a hurry and took a chance. But the time I reached Bolzano I was sorry I had done so. It was bitterly cold, and the sky ahead was leaden. At Merano I seriously considered turning back. Instead, I pushed on as hard as I could go. If I had had any sense I should have stopped for petrol before I started the really serious part of the climb. I had six gallons by the gauge then. I knew that it wasn't accurate, but I had filled up early that morning and calculated that I had enough to get me to Sargans. In my anxiety to beat the snow I overlooked the fact that I had miles of low-gear driving to do. On the Swiss side and on the Sargans road where it runs within a mile or two of the Rhätikon part of the German frontier, the car sputtered to a standstill.

For a minute or two I sat there swearing at and to myself and wondering what on earth I was going to do. I was, I knew, the only thing on the road that night for miles.

It was about eight o'clock, very dark and very cold. Except for the faint creaking of the cooling engine and the rustle of the breeze in some nearby trees, there wasn't a sound to be heard. Ahead, the road in the headlights curved away to the right. I got out the map and tried to find out where I was.

I had passed through one village since I had left Klosters, and I knew that it was about ten kilometres back. I must, therefore, either walk back ten kilometres to that village, or forward to the next village, whichever was the nearer. I looked at the map. It was of that useless kind that they sell to motorists. There was nothing marked between Klosters and Sargans. For all I knew, the next village might be fifteen or twenty kilometres away.

An Alpine road on a late November night is not the place to choose if you want to sleep in your car. I decided to walk back the way I had come.

I had a box of those small Italian waxed matches with me when I started out. There were, I thought, about a hundred in the box, and I calculated that, if I struck one every hundred metres, they would last until I reached the village.

That was when I was near the lights of the car. When I got out of sight of them, things were different. The darkness seemed to press against the backs of my eyes. It was almost painful. I could not even see the shape of the road along which I was walking. It was only by the rustling and the smell of resin that I knew that I was walking between fir trees. By the time I had covered a mile I had six matches left. Then it began to snow.

I say, 'snow'. It had been snow; but the Sargans road was still below the snow-line, and the stuff came down as a sort of half-frozen mush that slid down my face into the gap between my coat collar and my neck.

I must have done about another mile and a half when the real trouble began. I still had the six matches, but my hands were too numb to get them out of the box without wetting them, and I had been going forward blindly, sometimes on the road and sometimes off it. I was wondering whether I would get along better if I sang, when I walked into a telegraph post.

It was of pre-cast concrete and the edge was as sharp as a razor. My face was as numb as my hands and I didn't feel much except a sickening jar; but I could taste blood trickling between my teeth and found that my nose was bleeding. It was as I held my head back to stop it that I saw the light, looking for all the world as if it were suspended in mid-air above me.

It wasn't suspended in mid-air, and it wasn't above me. Darkness does strange things to perspective. After a few seconds I saw that it was showing through the trees on the hillside, up off the right of the road.

Anyone who has been in the sort of mess that I was in will know exactly how my mind worked at that moment. I did not speculate as to the origin of that God-forsaken light or as to whether or not the owner of it would be pleased to see me. I was cold and wet, my nose was bleeding, and I would not have cared if someone had told me that behind that light was a maniac with a machine-gun. I knew only that the light meant that there was some sort of human habitation near me and that I was going to spend the night in it.

I moved over to the other side of the road and began to feel my way along the wire fence I found there. Twenty yards or so farther on, my hands touched a wooden gate. The light was no longer visible, but I pushed the gate open and walked on into the blackness.

The ground rose steeply under my feet. It was a path of sorts, and soon I stumbled over the beginnings of a flight of log steps. There must have been well over a hundred of them. Then there was another stretch of path, not quite so steep. When I again saw the light, I was only about twenty yards from it.

It came from an oil reading-lamp standing near a window. From the shape of the window and the reflected light of the lamp, I could see that the place was a small chalet of the kind usually let to families for the summer season or for the winter sports. That it should be occupied at the end of November was curious. But I didn't ponder over the curiosity: I had seen something else through the window besides the lamp. The light from a fire was flickering in the room.

I went forward up the path to the door. There was no knocker. I hammered on the wet, varnished wood with my fist and waited. There was no sound from inside. After a moment or two I knocked again. Still there was no sign of life within. I knocked and waited for several minutes. Then I began to shiver. In desperation I grabbed the latch of the door and rattled it violently. The next moment I felt it give and the door creaked open a few inches.

I think that I have a normal, healthy respect for the property and privacy of my fellow-creatures; but at that moment I was feeling neither normal nor healthy. Obviously, the owner of the chalet could not be far away. I stood there for a moment or two, hesitating. I could smell the wood smoke from the fire, and mingled with it a bitter, oily smell that seemed faintly familiar. But all I cared about was the fire. I hesitated no longer and walked in.

14

As soon as I was inside I saw that there was something more than curious about the place, and that I should have waited.

The room itself was ordinary enough. It was rather larger than I had expected, but there were the usual pinewood walls, the usual pinewood floor, the usual pinewood staircase up to the bedrooms, and the usual tiled fireplace. There were the usual tables and chairs, too: turned and painted nonsense of the kind that sometimes finds its way into English tea-shops. There were red gingham curtains over the windows. You felt that the owner probably had lots of other places just like it, and that he made a good thing out of letting them.

No, it was what had been added to the room that was curious. All the furniture had been crowded into one half of the space. In the other half, standing on linoleum and looking as if it were used a good deal, was a printing press.

The machine was a small treadle platen of the kind used by jobbing printers for running off tradesmen's circulars. It looked very old and decrepit. Alongside it on a trestle-table were a case of type and a small proofing press with a locked-up forme in it. On a second table stood a pile of interleaved sheets, beside which was a stack of what appeared to be some of the same sheets folded. The folding was obviously being done by hand. I picked up one of the folded sheets.

It looked like one of those long, narrow, business-promotion folders issued by travel agencies. The front page was devoted to the reproduction, in watery blue ink, of a lino-cut of a clump of pines on the shore of a lake, and the display of the word TITISEE. Page two and the page folded in to face it carried a rhapsodical account in German of the beauties of Baden in general and Lake Titisee in particular.

I put the folder down. An inaccessible Swiss chalet was an odd place to choose for printing German travel advertisements; but I was not disposed to dwell on its oddity. I was cold.

I was moving towards the fire when my eye was caught by five words printed in bold capitals on one of the unfolded sheets on the table: 'DEUTSCHE MÄNNER UND FRAUEN, KAMERADEN!'

I stood still. I remember that my heart thudded against my ribs as suddenly and violently as it had earlier that day on the

15

Stelvio when some crazy fool in a Hispano had nearly crowded me off the road.

I leaned forward, picked the folder up again, and opened it right out. The message began on the second of the three inside pages.

'GERMAN MEN AND WOMEN, COMRADES! We speak to you with the voice of German Democracy, bringing you news. Neither Nazi propaganda nor the Gestapo can silence us, for we have an ally which is proof against floggings, an ally which no man in the history of the world has been able to defeat. That ally is Truth. Hear then, people of Germany, the Truth which is concealed from you. Hear it, remember it, and repeat it. The sooner the Truth is known, the sooner will Germany again hold up its head among the free nations of the world.'

Then followed a sort of news bulletin consisting chiefly of facts and figures (especially figures) about the economic condition of Germany. There was also news of a strike in the Krupp works at Essen and a short description of a riot outside a shipyard in Hamburg.

I put it down again. Now I knew why these 'travel advertisements' were being printed in an inaccessible Swiss chalet instead of in Germany itself. No German railway official would distribute these folders. That business would be left to more desperate men. These folders would not collect dust on the counters of travel agencies. They would be found in trains and in trams, in buses and in parked cars, in waiting-rooms and in bars, under restaurant plates and inside table napkins. Some of the men that put them there would be caught and tortured to betray their fellows; but the distribution would go on. The folders would be read, perhaps furtively discussed. A little more truth would seep through Goebbels' dam of lies to rot still further the creaking foundations of Nazidom.

Then, as I stood there with the smell of wood smoke and printing ink in my nostrils, as I stood staring at that decrepit little machine as if it were the very voice of freedom, I heard footsteps outside.

I suppose that I should have stood my ground. I had, after all, a perfectly good explanation of my presence there. My car and the blood from my nose would confirm my story. But I didn't reason that way. I had stumbled on a secret, and my first impulse was to try to hide the fact from the owner of the secret. I obeyed that impulse.

I looked round quickly and saw the stairs. Before I had even begun to wonder if I might not be doing something excessively stupid, I was up the stairs and opening the first door I came to on the landing. In the half-light I caught a glimpse of a bed; then I was inside the room with the door slightly ajar. I could see across the landing and through the wooden palings along it to the top of the window at the far side of the room below.

I knew that someone had come in: I could hear him moving about. He lit another lamp. There was a sound from the door and a second person entered.

A woman's voice said in German, 'Thank God, Johann has left a good fire.'

There was an answering grunt. It came from the man. I could almost feel them warming their hands.

'Get the coffee, Freda,' said the man suddenly. 'I must go back soon.'

'But Bruno is there. You should take a little rest first.'

'Bruno is a Berliner. He is not as used to the cold as I am. If Kurt should come now he would be tired. Bruno could only look after himself.'

There was silence for a moment. Then the woman spoke again.

'Do you really think that he will come now, Stephan? It is so late.' She paused. Her voice had sounded casual, elaborately casual; but now, as she went on, there was an edge to it that touched the nerves. 'I can keep quite calm about it, you see, Stephan. I wish to believe, but it is so late, isn't it? You don't think he will come now, do you? Admit it.'

He laughed, but too heartily. 'You are too nervous, Freda. Kurt can take care of himself. He knows all the tricks now. He may have been waiting for the first snow. The frontier guards would not be so alert on a night like this.'

'He should have been back a week ago. You know that as well as I do, Stephan. He has never been delayed so long before. They have got him. That is all. You see, I can be calm about it even though he is my dear husband.' And then her voice broke. 'I knew it would happen sooner or later. I knew it. First Hans, then Karl, and now Kurt. Those swine, those –'

17

She sobbed and broke suddenly into passionate weeping. He tried helplessly to comfort her.

I had heard enough. I was shaking from head to foot; but whether it was the cold or not, I don't know. I stood back from the door. Then, as I did so, I heard a sound from behind me.

I had noticed the bed as I had slipped into the room, but the idea that there might be someone in it had not entered my head. Now, as I whipped round, I saw that I had made a serious mistake.

Sitting on the edge of the bed in which he had been lying was a very thin, middle-aged man in a nightshirt. By the faint light from the landing I could see his eyes, bleary from sleep, and his grizzled hair standing ludicrously on end. But for one thing I should have laughed. That one thing was the large automatic pistol that he held pointed at me. His hand was as steady as a rock.

'Don't move,' he said. He raised his voice. 'Stephan! Come quickly!'

'I must apologize . . .' I began in German.

'You will be allowed to speak later.'

I heard Stephan dash up the stairs.

'What is it, Johann?'

'Come here.'

The door was pushed open behind me. I heard him draw in his breath sharply.

'Who is it?'

'I don't know. I was awakened by a noise. I was about to get up when this man came into the room. He did not see me. He has been listening to your conversation. He must have been examining the plant when he heard you returning.'

'If you will allow me to explain . . .'

'You may explain downstairs,' said the man called Stephan. 'Give me the pistol, Johann.'

The pistol changed hands and I could see Stephan, a lean, rawboned fellow with broad, sharp shoulders and dangerous eyes. He wore black oilskins and gum-boots. I saw the muscles in his cheeks tighten.

'Raise your hands and walk downstairs. Slowly. If you run, I shall shoot immediately. March.'

I went downstairs.

18

The woman, Freda, was standing by the door, staring blankly up at me as I descended. She must have been about thirty and had that soft rather matronly look about her that is character-istic of so many young German women. She was short and plump, and as if to accentuate the face, her straw-coloured hair was plaited across her head. Wisps of the hair had become detached and clung wetly to the sides of her neck. She too wore a black oilskin coat and gum-boots.

The grey eyes, red and swollen with crying, looked beyond me.

'Who is it, Stephan?'

'He was hiding upstairs.'

We had reached the foot of the stairs. He motioned me away from the door and towards the fire. 'Now, we will hear your explanation.'

I gave it with profuse apologies. I admitted that I had examined the folders and read one. 'It seemed to me,' I concluded, 'that my presence might be embarrassing to you. I was about to leave when you returned. Then, I am afraid, I lost my head and attempted to hide.'

Not one of them was believing a word that I was saying: I could see that from their faces. 'I assure you,' I went on in exasperation, 'that what I am telling . . .'

'What nationality are you?'

'British. I . . .'

'Then speak English. What were you doing on this road?'

'I am on my way home from Belgrade. I crossed the Yugoslav frontier yesterday and the Italian frontier at Stelvio this afternoon. My passport was stamped at both places if you wish to . . .'

'Why were you in Belgrade?'

'I am a surgeon. I have been attending an international medical convention there.'

'Let me see your passport, please.'

'Certainly. I have . . .' And then with my hand in my inside pocket, I stopped. My heart felt as if it had come right into my throat. In my haste to be away after the Italian Customs had finished with me, I had thrust my passport with the customs carnet for the car into the pocket beside me on the door of the car.

19

They were watching me with expressionless faces. Now, as my hand reappeared empty, I saw Stephan raise his pistol.

'Well?'

'I am sorry.' Like a fool I had begun to speak in German again. 'I find that I have left my passport in my car. It is several kilometres along the road. If . . .'

And then the woman burst.out as if she couldn't stand listening to me any longer.

'Don't you see? Don't you see?' she cried. 'It is quite clear. They have found out that we are here. Perhaps after all these months Hans or Karl has been tortured by them into speaking. And so they have taken Kurt and sent this man to spy upon us. It is clear. Don't you see?'

She turned suddenly, and I thought she was going to attack me. Then Stephan put his hand on her arm.

'Gently, Freda.' He turned to me again, and his expression hardened. 'You see, my friend, what is in our minds? We know our danger, you see. The fact that we are in Swiss territory will not protect us if the Gestapo should trace us. The Nazis, we know, have little respect for frontiers. The Gestapo have none. They would murder us here as confidently as they would if we were in the Third Reich. We do not underrate their cunning. The fact that you are not a German is not conclusive. You may be what you say you are; you may not. If you are, so much the better. If not, then I give you fair warning, you will be shot. You say that your passport is in your car several kilometres along the road. Unfortunately, it is not possible for us to spare time tonight to see if that is true. Nor is it possible for one of us to stand guard over you all night. You have already disturbed the first sleep Johann has had in twenty-four hours. There is only one thing for it, I'm afraid. It is undignified and barbaric; but I see no other way. We shall be forced to tie you up so that you cannot leave.'

'But this is absurd,' I cried angrily. 'Good heavens, man, I realize that I've only myself to blame for being here; but surely you could have the common decency to . . .'

'The question,' he said sternly, 'is not of decency, but of necessity. We have no time tonight for six-kilometre walks. One of our comrades has been delivering a consignment of these folders to our friends in Germany. We hope and believe that he will return to us across the frontier tonight. He may need our help. Mountaineering in such weather is exhausting. Freda, get me some of the cord we use for tying the packages.'

I wanted to say something, but the words would not come. I was too angry. I don't think that I've ever been so angry in my life before.

She brought the cord. It was thick grey stuff. He took it and gave the pistol to Johann. Then he came towards me.

I don't think they liked the business any more than I did. He had gone a bit white and he wouldn't look me in the eyes. I think that I must have been white myself; but it was anger with me. He put the cord under one of my elbows. I snatched it away.

'You had better submit,' he said harshly.

'To spare your feelings? Certainly not. You'll have to use force, my friend. But don't worry. You'll get used to it. You'll be a good Nazi yet. You should knock me down. That'll make it easier.'

What colour there was left in his face went. A good deal of my anger evaporated at that moment. I felt sorry for the poor devil. I really believe that I should have let him tie me up. But I never knew for certain; for at that moment there was an interruption.

It was the woman who heard it first – the sound of someone running up the path outside. The next moment a man burst wildly into the room.

Stephan had turned. 'Bruno! What is it? Why aren't you at the hut?'

The man was striving to get his breath, and for a moment he could hardly speak. His face above the streaming oilskins was blue with cold. Then he gasped out, 'Kurt! He is at the hut! He is wounded – badly!'

The woman gave a little whimpering cry and her hands went to her face. Stephan gripped the newcomer's shoulder.

'What has happened? Quickly!'

'It was dark. The Swiss did not see him. It was one of our patrols. They shot him when he was actually on the Swiss side. He was wounded in the thigh. He crawled on to the hut, but he can go no farther. He . . .'

But Stephan had ceased to listen. He turned sharply. 'Johann, you must dress yourself at once. Bruno, take the pistol and guard this man. He broke in here. He may be dangerous. Freda, get the cognac and the iodine. We shall need them for Kurt.'

He himself went to a cupboard and got out some handkerchiefs, which he began tearing feverishly into strips, which he knotted together. Still gasping for breath, the man Bruno had taken the pistol and was staring at me with a puzzled frown. Then the woman reappeared from the kitchen carrying a bottle of cognac and a small phial of iodine of the sort that is sold for dabbing on cut fingers. Stephan stuffed them in his pockets with the knotted handkerchiefs. Then he called up the stairs, 'Hurry, Johann. We are ready to leave.'

It was more than I could bear. Professional fussiness, I suppose.

'Has any one of you,' I asked loudly, 'ever dealt with a bullet wound before?'

They stared at me. Then Stephan glanced at Bruno.

'If he moves,' he said, 'shoot.' He raised his voice again. 'Johann!'

There was an answering cry of reassurance.

'Has it occurred to you,' I persisted, 'that even if you get him here alive, which I doubt, as you obviously don't know what you're doing, he will need immediate medical attention? Don't you think that one of you had better go for a doctor? Ah, but of course; the doctor would ask questions about a bullet wound, wouldn't he? The matter would be reported to the police.'

'We can look after him,' he grunted. 'Johann! Hurry!'

'It seems a pity,' I said reflectively, 'that one brave man should have to die because of his friends' stupidity.' And then my calm deserted me. 'You damn fool!' I shouted. 'Listen to me. Do you want to kill this man? You're going about it the right way. I'm a surgeon, and this is a surgeon's business. Take that cognac out of your pocket. We shan't need it. The iodine too. And those pieces of rag. Have you got two or three clean towels?'

The woman nodded stupidly.

'Then get them, please, and be quick. And you said something about some coffee. Have you a flask for it? Good. Then we shall take that. Put plenty of sugar in it. I want blankets, too. Three will be enough, but they must be kept dry.

We shall need a stretcher. Get two poles or broomsticks and two old coats. We can make a stretcher of sorts by putting the poles through the sleeves of them. Take this cord of yours too. It will be useful to make slings for the stretcher. And hurry! The man may be bleeding to death. Is he far away?'

The man was glowering at me. 'Four kilometres. In a climbing hut in the hills this side of the frontier.' He stepped forward and gripped my arm. 'If you are tricking us . . .' he began.

'I'm not thinking about you,' I snapped. 'I'm thinking about a man who's been crawling along with a bullet in his thigh and a touching faith in his friends. Now get those poles, and hurry.'

They hurried. In three minutes they had the things collected. The exhausted Bruno's oilskins and gum-boots had, at my suggestion, been transferred to me. Then I tied one of the blankets round my waist under my coat, and told Stephan and Johann to do the same.

'I,' said the woman, 'will take the other things.'

'You,' I said, 'will stay here, please.'

She straightened up at that. 'No,' she said firmly. 'I will come with you. I shall be quite calm. You will see.'

'Nevertheless,' I said rather brutally, 'you will be more useful here. A bed must be ready by the fire here. There must also be hot bricks and plenty of blankets. I shall need, besides, both boiled and boiling water. You have plenty of ordinary salt, I suppose?'

'Yes, *Herr Doktor*. But . . .'

'We are wasting time.'

Two minutes later we left.

I shall never forget that climb. It began about half a mile along the road below the chalet. The first part was mostly up narrow paths between trees. They were covered with pine needles and, in the rain, as slippery as the devil. We had been climbing steadily for about half an hour when Stephan, who had been leading the way with a storm lantern, paused.

'I must put out the light here,' he said. 'The frontier is only three kilometres from here, and the guards patrol to a depth of two kilometres. They must not see us.' He blew out the lamp. 'Turn round,' he said then. 'You will see another light.'

I saw it, far away below us, a pin-point.

23

'That's our light. When we are returning from Germany, we can see it from across the frontier and know that we are nearly home and that our friends are waiting. Hold on to my coat now. You need not worry about Johann behind you. He knows the path well. This way, *Herr Doktor.*'

It was the only sign he gave that he had decided to accept me for what I said I was.

I cannot conceive of how anyone could know that path well. The surface soon changed from pine needles to a sort of rocky rubble, and it twisted and turned like a wounded snake. The wind had dropped, but it was colder than ever, and I found myself crunching through sugary patches of half-frozen slush. I wondered how on earth we were going to bring down a wounded man on an improvised stretcher.

We had been creeping along without the light for about twenty minutes when Stephan stopped and, shielding the lamp with his coat, relit it. I saw that we had arrived.

The climbing hut was built against the side of an overhanging rock face. It was about six feet square inside, and the man was lying diagonally across it on his face. There was a large bloodstain on the floor beneath him. He was semi-conscious. His eyes were closed, but he mumbled something as I felt for his pulse.

'Will he live?' whispered Stephan.

I didn't know. The pulse was there, but it was feeble and rapid. His breathing was shallow. I looked at the wound. The bullet had entered on the inner side of the left thigh just below the groin. There was a little bleeding, but it obviously hadn't touched the femoral artery and, as far as I could see, the bone was all right. I made a dressing with one of the towels and tied it in place with another. The bullet could wait. The immediate danger was from shock aggravated by exposure. I got to work with the blankets and the flask of coffee. Soon the pulse strengthened a little, and after about half an hour I told them how to prepare the stretcher.

I don't know how they got him down that path in the darkness. It was all I could do to get down by myself. It was snowing hard now in great fleecy chunks that blinded you when you moved forward. I was prepared for them to slip and drop the stretcher; but they didn't. It was slow work, however, and it was a good forty minutes before we got to the point where it was safe to light the lamp.

After that I was able to help with the stretcher. At the foot of the path up to the chalet, I went ahead with the lantern. The woman heard my footsteps and came to the door. I realized that we must have been gone for the best part of three hours.

'They're bringing him up,' I said. 'He'll be all right. I shall need your help now.'

She said, 'The bed is ready.' And then, 'Is it serious, *Herr Doktor?*'

'No.' I didn't tell her then that there was a bullet to be taken out.

It was a nasty job. The wound itself wasn't so bad. The bullet must have been pretty well spent, for it had lodged up against the bone without doing any real damage. It was the instruments that made it difficult. They came from the kitchen. He didn't stand up to it very well, and I wasn't surprised. I didn't feel so good myself when I'd finished. The cognac came in useful after all.

We finally got him to sleep about five.

'He'll be all right now,' I said.

The woman looked at me and I saw the tears begin to trickle down her cheeks. It was only then that I remembered that she wasn't a nurse, but his wife.

It was Johann who comforted her. Stephan came over to me.

'We owe you a great debt, *Herr Doktor,*' he said. 'I must apologize for our behaviour earlier this evening. We have not always been savages, you know. Kurt was a professor of zoology. Johann was a master printer. I was an architect. Now we are those who crawl across frontiers at night and plot like criminals. We have been treated like savages, and so we live like them. We forget sometimes that we were civilized. We ask your pardon. I do not know how we can repay you for what you have done. We . . .'

But I was too tired for speeches. I smiled quickly at him.

'All that I need by way of a fee is another glass of cognac and a bed to sleep in for a few hours. I suggest, by the way, that you get a doctor in to look at the patient later today. There will be a little fever to treat. Tell the doctor he fell upon his climbing axe. He won't believe you, but there'll be no bullet for him to be inquisitive about. Oh, and if you could find me a little petrol for my car . . .'

It was five in the afternoon and almost dark again when Stephan woke me. The local doctor, he reported, as he set an enormous tray of food down beside the bed, had been, dressed the wound, prescribed, and gone. My car was filled up with petrol and awaited me below if I wished to drive to Zürich that night. Kurt was awake and could not be prevailed upon to sleep until he had thanked me.

They were all there, grouped about the bed, when I went downstairs. Bruno was the only one who looked as if he had had any sleep.

He sprang to his feet. 'Here, Kurt,' he said facetiously, 'is the *Herr Doktor*. He is going to cut your leg off.'

Only the woman did not laugh at the jest. Kurt himself was smiling when I bent over to look at him.

He was a youngish-looking man of about forty with intelligent brown eyes and a high, wide forehead. The smile faded from his face as he looked at me.

'You know what I wish to say, *Herr Doktor?*'

I took refuge in professional brusqueness. 'The less you say, the better,' I said, and felt for his pulse. But as I did so his fingers moved and gripped my hand.

'One day soon,' he said, 'England and the Third Reich will be at war. But you will not be at war with Germany. Remember that, please, *Herr Doktor*. Not with Germany. It is people like us who are Germany, and in our way we shall fight with England. You will see.'

I left soon after.

At nine that night I was in Zürich.

Llewellyn was back in the room. I put the manuscript down. He looked across at me.

'Very interesting,' I said.

'I'd considered sending it up to one of these magazines that publish short stories,' he said apologetically. 'I thought I'd like your opinion first, though. What do you think?'

I cleared my throat. 'Well, of course, it's difficult to say. Very interesting, as I said. But there's no real point to it, is there? It needs something to tie it all together.'

'Yes, I see what you mean. It sort of leaves off, doesn't it? But that's how it actually happened.' He looked disappointed. 'I don't think I could invent an ending. It would be rather a pity, wouldn't it? You see, it's all true.'

'Yes, it would be a pity.'

'Well, anyway, thanks for reading it. Funny thing to happen. I really only put it down on paper for fun. Have another brandy?' He got up. 'Oh, by the way. I was forgetting. I heard from those people about a week after war broke out. A letter. Let's see now, where did I put it? Ah, yes.'

He rummaged in a drawer for a bit, and then, tossing a letter over to me, picked up the brandy bottle.

The envelope bore a Swiss stamp and the postmark was Klosters, September 4th, 1939. The contents felt bulky. I drew them out.

The cause of the bulkiness was what looked like a travel agent's folder doubled up to fit the envelope. I straightened it. On the front page was a lino-cut of a clump of pines on the shore of a lake and the word TITISEE. I opened out the folder.

'GERMAN MEN AND WOMEN, COMRADES!' The type was worn and battered. 'Hitler has led you into war. He fed you with lies about the friendly Polish people. In your name he has now committed a wanton act of aggression against them. As a consequence, the free democracies of England and France have declared war against Germany. Comrades, right and justice are on their side. It is Hitler and National Socialism who are the enemies of peace in Europe. Our place as true Germans is at the side of the democracies against Hitler, against National Socialism. Hitler cannot win this war. But the people of Germany must act. All Germans, Catholics, Protestants, and Jews, must act now. Our Czech and Slovak friends are already refusing to make guns for Hitler. Let us stand by their sides. Remember . . .'

I was about to read on when I saw that the letter that accompanied the folder had fluttered to the carpet. I picked it up. It consisted of a few typewritten lines on an otherwise blank sheet of paper.

Greetings, Herr Doktor. We secured your address from the Customs carnet in your car and write now to wish you good luck. Kurt, Stephan, and Bruno have made many journeys since we saw you and returned safely each time. Today, Kurt leaves again. We pray for him *as always. With this letter we send you Johann's newest work so that you shall see that Kurt spoke the truth to you. We are of the army of the shadows. We do not fight for you against our countrymen; but we fight with you against National Socialism, our common enemy.*

Auf Wiedersehen,
FREDA, KURT, STEPHAN, JOHANN, AND BRUNO.

Llewellyn put my glass down on the table beside me. 'Help yourself to a cigarette. What do you think of that? Nice of them, wasn't it?' he added. 'Sentimental lot, these Germans.'

End of the
Beginning

THE Army of the Shadows was written to meet a deadline and my haste still shows. Given more time I could have made the story crisper and the telling of it less John Buchanish. Still, the writing of it, and perhaps the deadline too, proved oddly stimulating. For the first time since that night in Harry's Bar and the news of the infamous Pact I began to think it possible that my career as a writer might not after all be quite over. True, I was waiting to get into the Navy and did not want to start a new novel that I might not have time to finish, but I still had the habit of writing every day, a habit which I had cultivated and one with which I was always comfortable. When my agent reported that a weekly magazine the *Sketch* wanted to commission from me a series of six short detective stories, I accepted immediately.

Rash? I suppose so. I had never tried to write a detective story, but I had read the great masters of the genre, admired their fearsome ingenuity and deplored the faintly ridiculous set of 'rules' for their craft laid down by the early paladins of The Detection Club. The Father Brown short stories of G. K. Chesterton had entertained me, not least because of the author's effrontery in endowing his detective with a private line to God. Any approach of mine to the puzzle problem was bound to be less fanciful, but at least it could be workmanlike. I must not disgrace myself by cheating the reader. My plots must work.

That was the week my orders came. They were to report to Room So-and-So at the Admiralty for an interview. I did and had a bad time. The list my friend in the Ministry had put me on was one for men capable of skippering minesweeping trawlers in the North Sea. The essential qualifications were deep-sea

31

yachting experience, membership of a recognized yacht club, and an ability to navigate. The interviewing officer was a polite bastard with a humiliating smile. I could have murdered him as well as the friend who thought that all writers of thirty could or should be amateur yachtsmen. Instead, with murder in my heart, I wandered across Trafalgar Square to the Charing Cross Road. There I bought a secondhand copy of Taylor's *Principles and Practice of Medical Jurisprudence*, then the standard general work on the science of forensic medicine, a murderer's vademecum.

Taylor came in two volumes. The first dealt with bodily harm resulting from external violence – blows, falls, stabbings, strangulation, fire, gunshot wounds, and other mayhem. The second volume was all about poisons. A couple of days' browsing gave me the technical material for six cosy little murder mysteries; six little puzzles with six solutions that could be explained briefly and without elaborate dissection of alibis. A suitable master detective was needed. He would have to fit into small narrative spaces. His entrances and exits must have a clear pattern. He must belong noticeably to the times we were living in. He must be a refugee.

Dr Czissar, my refugee Czech detective, was based on two real refugees from Nazi persecution. I had known them both before the war; one a Prague newspaper editor, the other a German historian deprived of his academic post for being part Jewish. The flapping raincoat and the umbrella carried like a rifle were stage props added when I began to write. The historian was the author of a highly praised history of the German army, so it seemed to me right that Czissar should have a soldierly Prussian manner.

The Intrusions of Dr Czissar passed the time between the refusal of my services by the Admiralty and their curt rejection by the RAF – 'What the hell do you expect us to have for a thirty-year-old writer? Try the army.' Louise Crombie and I were married in the local town hall, a civil ceremony conducted by the Registrar of Births, Marriages and Deaths. A certain piquancy was added to the occasion by our being in possession of inside information. In that London suburb the deaths expected in the first serious air-raid would number about five thousand, and collapsible utility coffins to contain the corpses had been ordered by the man who married us. They were already stored in the town hall cellars below us.

I took a course in First Aid for stretcher-bearers.

The Intrusions of Dr Czissar:
The Case of the Pinchbeck Locket

THE winter afternoon on which Dr Jan Czissar chose to
introduce his peculiar personality into the life of Assistant-
Commissioner Mercer of Scotland Yard was cold and depressing. And Mercer, besides having a cold and being depressed,
was also busy. Had Dr Czissar not been in possession of a
letter of introduction from, as Sergeant Flecker put it, 'one of
the 'Ome Office brass 'ats,' he would not have seen the
Assistant-Commissioner at all.

The letter was brief. Having presented his compliments, the
writer said that Dr Jan Czissar had been, until the September of
1938, a distinguished member of the Czech police organization,
that he was a welcome guest in this country, and that any
courtesy which could be extended to him by the Assistant-
Commissioner would be very much appreciated. It was not
until it was too late to save himself that Mercer found that the
letter, though brief, was by no means to the point.

Mercer had dealt with distinguished visitors to Scotland Yard
before. There would be the preliminary exchange of courtesies,
then a tour of the buildings, conducted by Inspector Denton,
who would appear, as if by accident, a few moments after the
visitor had entered Mercer's room, and, finally, the farewell
handshake and a safe conduct to the Embankment entrance and
a taxi.

In spite, therefore, of his cold and his depression and his
interrupted work, it was with a smile that Mercer greeted Dr
Czissar's entry into his room.

Dr Czissar was a plump, middle-aged man of rather more
than medium height, with a round, pale face and a pair of sad,
brown eyes, magnified to cow-like proportions by a pair of thick
pebble glasses. He wore a long grey raincoat, which reached

35

nearly to his ankles, and carried an unfurled umbrella. As he came into the room he stopped, clicked his heels, clapped the umbrella to his side as if it were a rifle, bowed, and said loudly and distinctly: 'Doctor Jan Czissar. Late Prague police. At your service.'

'Delighted, Doctor. Won't you take a seat?'

Dr Czissar took a seat. His cow-like eyes blinked round the room and came to rest once more on Mercer.

'It is good of you,' said the Doctor suddenly, 'to see me so promptly. It is an honour to be received at Scotland Yard. In common with my colleagues' – the cow-like eyes narrowed slightly – 'my *late* colleagues of the Czech police, I have always admired your institution.'

Mercer was used to dealing with this sort of thing. He smiled deprecatingly. 'We do our best. Ours is a law-abiding country.' And then his ears caught the sound they had been waiting for – the sound of Inspector Denton's footsteps approaching along the corridor. He rose to his feet. 'Well, Doctor, now that you're here, I expect you'd like to see something of our organization, eh?'

Time had given the question a purely rhetorical significance for Mercer. For him, Dr Czissar was already safely under the wing of the approaching Inspector Denton. The words of introduction were already rising to his lips, the Inspector was already rapping dutifully at the door, the machinery for the speedy disposal of distinguished visitors was getting smoothly under way: and then, the unbelievable happened.

Dr Czissar said: 'Oh no, thank you. I will not trouble.'

For a moment Mercer thought that he had misunderstood.

'It's no trouble at all, Doctor.'

'Some other day, perhaps.' The cow-like eyes regarded him kindly. 'I am rather busy, you know. A text-book of medical jurisprudence. Perhaps if we could have a little talk about an important matter in which I am interested it would be better.'

Mercer subsided slowly into his chair. He saw Denton was standing helplessly inside the door. He heard Sergeant Flecker, at his desk in the corner, say 'Crikey!' a little too loudly. Dr Czissar's large, sad eyes regarded him compassionately. He strove to render his face and voice expressionless.

'Well, Doctor. What can we do for you?'

36

'Pardon, Assistant-Commissioner Mercer. It is I who can do something for you.'

'Ah, yes?'

And then Mercer witnessed, for the first of many times, the spectacle of Dr Czissar going into action. A faint, thin smile stretched the Doctor's full lips. He settled his glasses on his nose. Then he produced an enormous alligator-skin wallet and took from it a newspaper cutting. Finally, he performed a series of three actions which Mercer was going in time to recognize and to detest. He cleared his throat, swallowed hard, and then said sharply: 'Attention, please!'

'I think,' he added slowly, 'that I can help you to discover a crime. Clever criminals are so stupid, are they not?'

Mercer stroked his chin. A warm, comfortable feeling suffused his breast. This Czech was just another lunatic, after all. Unhinged, no doubt, by his experiences as a refugee. He thought of the memorandum he would send the 'brass hat' in the Home Office and smiled benignly on Dr Czissar. Once more he got to his feet.

'Very good of you. Now, if you'll just put the whole thing in writing and post it to me, we'll look into it.'

Dr Czissar's thin smile vanished. The cow-like eyes flashed. 'It is unnecessary. The matter is in writing and here.' He put the newspaper cutting under Mercer's nose. 'Please,' he said firmly, 'to read.'

Again Mercer sat down. His eyes met those of Dr Czissar. He read.

The cutting was from a Wessex weekly newspaper dated a fortnight previously, and was the report of an inquest. The body of a woman of sixty had been washed up in Shingles Bay and had been identified as that of Mrs Sarah Fallon, of Seahurst, a village five miles from the seaside resort of Seabourne. Her husband had died fifteen years earlier, leaving her a large fortune and Seahurst Grange, with its twenty-acre park. Soon after his death she had assumed the guardianship of his niece, Helen Fallon, who had married, eleven years later, Arthur Barrington, a Seabourne coal and builders' merchant, and President of the Seabourne Angling Society. The Barringtons had lived since their marriage with Mrs Fallon at the Grange.

On the evening of November 4 Barrington had reported to the police that Mrs Fallon had disappeared. That afternoon Mrs Barrington had, at her aunt's request, driven her into Sea-bourne to do some shopping. As Mrs Fallon had said that she might call on a friend for tea, her niece had left her at South Square at a quarter to three, put the car in the municipal car park, and spent the afternoon in a cinema. They had arranged to meet at South Square at six o'clock. Mrs Fallon had not kept the appointment, and later, when attempts to trace her movements through her friends had failed, the police had been informed.

She had not been seen again until eight days later, when her body was found by a coastguard.

Evidence of identification was given by her doctor and her dentist. The post-mortem had revealed the cause of death as being shock following a fracture of the skull. The fracture could have been caused by violent contact with any blunt, hard surface. It would have been consistent with a fall from a high cliff. She had not entered the water until several hours after death. The state of decomposition suggested that she had probably died on the date of her disappearance. Her doctor added that she had suffered from a cardiac disturbance and was liable to spells of dizziness.

A child, Annie Smith, had given evidence of the finding, on the seventh of the month, of a heart-shaped pinchbeck locket at the foot of Sea Head Cliff, a local beauty spot within a few minutes' walk of South Square.

Mrs Barrington had identified the locket as having belonged to her aunt. Her aunt, who had attached great sentimental value to the locket, had always worn it. Her aunt had been in the habit of sitting on the seat on the cliff during the afternoon. She had not, however, done so for several days prior to her disappearance as she had had a cold.

The coroner, summing up, had said that there seemed very little doubt that the deceased had, after she had left her niece on the afternoon of the fourth, changed her mind about visiting her friends and walked up the hill to the cliff. Then, fatigued by the walk after her recent illness, she had had an attack of giddiness and fallen to her death on the beach below. High tide had been at six o'clock. Her body must have lain on the beach until ultimately it had been carried out to sea.

A verdict of 'Accidental Death' had been returned, the jury adding a rider to the effect that the cliff should be fenced.

Mercer looked up. 'Well, Doctor?'

'Mrs Fallon,' said Dr Czissar decisively, 'was, I think, murdered.'

Mercer sighed and leaned back in his chair.

'Sergeant,' he said, 'get me the file on the Fallon case, will you?' He smiled wearily at the Doctor. 'You see, Doctor, we are not so stupid. A rich woman meets with an accident. Her niece, who lives in her house, inherits. The niece's husband, who also lives in the house, happens to be in financial difficulties in his business. The Chief Constable of Wessex thought it advisable to ask us to look into the matter. Ah, thank you, Sergeant. Here we are, Doctor. All open and above board. The niece first.

'She spent the afternoon as she says she did. Car-park and cinema attendants both confirm that she spent the afternoon at Seabourne. She arrived home at seven, having waited for half an hour in South Square and spent ten minutes or so telephoning her aunt's friends. Barrington returned home soon afterwards. He had left at two thirty to keep a business appointment in Haywick – that's fourteen miles farther west along the coast – at three. He kept the appointment, and several others that he had made in the Haywick district for that afternoon. Anyway, no murderer in his senses would try to push anybody off the cliff. There's a coastguard station a quarter of a mile away. He would be too scared of being seen. Satisfied, Doctor?'

Dr Czissar's thin smile had reappeared. He nodded. 'Oh, yes. Quite satisfied. She was undoubtedly murdered. Were the servants at the Grange questioned?'

Mercer swallowed hard. 'Naturally.'

'And did any of them report any trouble with the heating arrangements on the night of Mrs Fallon's disappearance?'

Mercer restrained himself with an effort. He turned slowly to Inspector Denton. 'Well, Inspector? You went down to Seahurst, didn't you? Can you answer the Doctor's question? By the way,' he added perfunctorily, 'this is Inspector Denton, Doctor.'

Dr Czissar sprang up like a Jack-in-the-box, clicked his heels, and sat down again.

39

The Inspector shifted uneasily. 'As a matter of fact,' he said, averting his eyes from his superior, 'there was some trouble with the heating, Sir. The housekeeper's a spiritualist, Sir, like myself, and she said they had trouble with the furnace that night. It went out. She reckoned that it was a sort of sign that the old lady had pegged out. Died,' he added by way of explanation, and relapsed into uncomfortable silence.

'Ah, so!' said Dr Czissar. His sad, brown eyes fastened again on Mercer's. 'Do you begin to see my argument, Assistant-Commissioner?'

Mercer stirred. 'To be frank with you, Doctor,' he said, 'I think that we are both wasting time.'

Dr Czissar smiled serenely. 'Attention, please,' he said. 'I will present the case to you.'

He raised one finger. 'First,' he said, 'the thing that attracts my attention is this matter of the locket. So curious, I think. It is found at the bottom of the cliff. Therefore, Mrs Fallon was killed by falling from the cliff. So simple. Perhaps a little *too* simple, do you think? It is found three days after the accident. Therefore it must have fallen on a place not covered by the tide. Six tides would certainly have buried it or swept it away, don't you think? Yesterday I went to Seabourne. I looked at the cliff. So interesting. It is quite impossible to drop an object from the top of the cliff so that it lands on the beach above the high-tide mark.'

Mercer shrugged. 'The clasp was broken. She probably clutched at it as she fell. She had heart trouble. It would be a natural gesture. It might fall anywhere under the circumstances.'

The brown eyes remained cow-like, but the full lips curled a little. 'Ah, so! It might. A woman of sixty in a poor state of health might also climb to the top of the cliff on a cold November day and stand near enough to the edge to fall over. But it is unlikely. And was she seen by the coastguards?'

'No. But that proves nothing. I think I should tell you, too, that the fact that she was washed up in Shingles Bay confirms the theory that she entered the water by the cliff. The currents are very strong there. From the cliff she would be certain to find her way to the bay.'

'Ah! She arrives in the Shingles Bay. Therefore she must have come from the cliff. Is that right?'

'There is the evidence of the locket.'

'Attention, please.' The thin smile had returned once more. 'I have made certain inquiries in Seabourne.'

'Indeed?'

'About the currents. You are, within limits, correct. There is a very strong current running past the cliff and across Firth Bay to the Shingles. But' – the eyes approached Mercer's quickly – 'this current sweeps along near the coast for some distance. It goes in very near to the coast at Haywick Dunes. And does it not occur to you, too, that eight days is a long time for a body to take to get from the cliff to Shingles Bay? The current is, as you said, a strong one.'

Mercer looked at Denton. 'Were we aware of these facts, Inspector?'

'No, Sir. The local men were quite sure about the cliff. They said they'd had one or two suicides from there and that the bodies all ended up in Shingles Bay.'

'I see. May I ask where you obtained this information, Doctor?'

'From the Secretary of the Seabourne Angling Society.' Dr Czissar coughed gently. 'Mr Barrington is the President of the Society this year, according to the newspaper. He, too, would know these things.'

'I see. Well, Doctor, this is all very interesting, but I am afraid –'

'Mrs Fallon,' continued Dr Czissar, 'was murdered for her money by Arthur and Helen Barrington, who, because they did not want to be found out, arranged alibis for themselves. They were not very useful alibis, because nobody knew exactly when Mrs Fallon was killed. In my opinion, she was killed between half past two and twenty-five minutes to three on the afternoon of her disappearance. She was placed in the sea at Haywick Dunes between six and seven o'clock that evening.'

'But –'

'The murder,' pursued Dr Czissar firmly, 'was very carefully thought out. You remember the drive up to the Grange, Inspector? It is long and winding, Assistant-Commissioner

Mercer, and most of it is invisible from the house because of trees.

'At half past two Barrington left to keep his appointment at Haywick. But instead of driving straight there, he stopped his car a little way down the road and walked back to the drive. Five minutes later his wife left to motor Mrs Fallon into Seabourne. As soon as she was out of sight of the house, but in the drive, she stopped. Her husband then killed Mrs Fallon with the weapon he had ready. A coal or mason's hammer would have been suitable. He was a coal and builders' merchant, I think. He then went back to his car and drove on to his appointment at Haywick. Mrs Barrington also drove on to Seabourne.'

'And where, pray, was the body?' inquired Mercer acidly.

'On the floor at the back of Mrs Barrington's car, with a rug covering it. They could not leave it among the trees, in case it should by chance be discovered. Barrington could not take it in his car. He had appointments to keep, and his car would be left in the road for long periods unattended. In the large municipal car park, Mrs Barrington's car would be safe from inspection. There is only one attendant, and he is at the gate.

'At half past five, I think, Mrs Barrington left the cinema, returned to her car, and drove to the Haywick Dunes, where she had arranged to meet her husband. High tide was at six o'clock. It must have been about then that they arranged to meet. It would be dusk then, too. And that place is very lonely and deserted. The chances of Barrington's being seen as he carried the body to the water were small, I think. No doubt Mrs Barrington then drove back to Seabourne to make the necessary inquiries of her aunt's friends. That is all, I think.'

There was silence for a moment. It was broken by the Inspector.

'I don't see where the furnace comes into it,' he remarked.

'The rug and the car mats would be soaked with blood, Inspector. Mrs Barrington would no doubt put them into the furnace after it had been banked-up for the night. Even such thick materials would be charred and destroyed, but they would put the fire out unless the dampers were also opened. Probably the niece of a rich aunt would not know much about furnaces.'

'However,' said Mercer sourly, 'you have yet, Dr Czissar, to explain the presence of the locket on the beach. They might, assuming that this – this theory of yours is correct, have taken the locket from the body. But I refuse to believe that they would, *after* the disappearance of Mrs Fallon, have risked detection by planting the locket on the beach. The risks would have been enormous, even at night. If he had been caught with it, why –'

'Ah, yes. The locket.' Dr Czissar smiled. 'I read about police matters in so many newspapers, you know, that I sometimes forget things I have read, even if they interested me. There is so much crime, is there not? Even in law-abiding England.' Was there, Mercer wondered, the faintest note of mockery in the fellow's voice? Confound him!

'It was,' said Dr Czissar, 'something I saw the other day in a second-hand jeweller's window that reminded me of the Barringtons.'

He put his hand in his pocket. It reappeared holding something that swung from a thin, yellow chain. It was a pinchbeck locket in the shape of a heart.

'The jeweller said,' went on Dr Czissar, 'that these things were quite common. Out of date, he said. One can buy such a locket almost anywhere if one tries. Perhaps there was one bought in Seabourne or Haywick recently. It could have been put on the beach on the night before the murder. After all, it was Mrs Barrington, wasn't it, who identified it as the particular locket that her aunt wore? Clever criminals are so stupid, are they not?'

He looked at his watch. 'I suggest also that you find out if Barrington purchased the new car mats and rug before or after the murder, and if anyone saw his wife driving towards Haywick on the fourth. And a detailed account of Barrington's movements after half past five would, no doubt, provide you with more of the evidence you need for a conviction.'

He got suddenly to his feet. 'But I must really be going. So kind of you. Enchanted. Enchanted.'

Mercer, in a daze, found himself returning once more the stiff little bow and the blank, cow-like stare. Then Dr Czissar was gone.

'Phew!' said the Inspector loudly. 'I thought –'

Mercer pulled himself together. 'I'll see you later, Denton,' he said sharply. 'Sergeant, see if you can find me some aspirin for this cold of mine.'

The door closed again and Mercer was alone.

He waited for a moment, staring hopelessly at the untouched pile of work in front of him. Then he drew a deep breath and picked up the telephone.

'I want,' he said, 'to speak to the Chief Constable of Wessex.'

The Case of the Emerald Sky

ASSISTANT-COMMISSIONER Mercer stared without speaking at the card which Sergeant Flecker had placed before him. There was no address: simply –

DR JAN CZISSAR

LATE PRAGUE POLICE

It was an inoffensive-looking card. An onlooker, who knew only that Dr Czissar was a refugee Czech, with a brilliant record of service in the criminal investigation department of the Prague police, would have been surprised at the expression of almost savage dislike that spread slowly over the Assistant-Commissioner's healthy face.

Yet, had the same onlooker known the circumstances of Mercer's first encounter with Dr Czissar, he would not have been so surprised. Just one week had elapsed since Dr Czissar had appeared out of the blue with a letter of intro-duction from the almighty Sir Herbert at the Home Office, and Mercer was still smarting as a result of the meeting. No man, least of all a man in charge of a criminal investigation, likes to be told, even very politely, that he doesn't know his job. When the teller not only tells, but proceeds to prove that he is right, pride is damaged. Mercer's expression can be excused.

Sergeant Flecker had seen and interpreted the expression. Now he spoke. 'Out, Sir?'

Mercer looked up sharply. 'No, Sergeant. In, but too busy!' he snapped, and got on with his work.

Half an hour later Mercer's telephone rang.

45

'Sir Herbert to speak to you from the Home Office, Sir,' said the male operator.

After a long and, to Mercer, extremely irritating interval, Sir Herbert came through.

'Hello, Mercer, is that you? I say, what's this I hear about your refusing to see Dr Czissar?'

Mercer jumped, but managed to pull himself together. 'I did not refuse to see him, Sir Herbert,' he said. 'I sent down a message that I was too busy to see him.'

Sir Herbert snorted. 'Now look here, Mercer. I happen to know that it was Dr Czissar who spotted those Seabourne murderers for you. Not blaming you personally, of course, and I don't propose to mention the matter to the Commissioner. You can't be right every time. We all know that as an organization there's nothing to touch Scotland Yard. My point is, Mercer, that you fellows ought not to be above learning a thing or two from a foreign expert. We don't want any of this professional jealousy. Of course' – there was a significant little pause – 'if you feel that it's a bit irregular, I can have a word with the Commissioner.'

If it were possible to speak coherently through clenched teeth, Mercer would have done so. 'There's no question of professional jealousy, Sir Herbert. I was, as Dr Czissar was informed, busy when he called. If he will write in for an appointment, I shall be pleased to see him.'

'Good man,' said Sir Herbert cheerfully. 'But we don't want any of this red-tape business about writing in. He's in my office now. I'll send him over. He's particularly anxious to have a word with you about this Brock Park case. Goodbye.'

Mercer replaced the telephone carefully. He knew that if he had replaced it as he felt like replacing it, the entire instrument would have been smashed. For a moment or two he sat quite still. Then, suddenly, he snatched the telephone up again.

'Inspector Cleat, please.' He waited. 'Is that you, Cleat? . . . Is the Commissioner in? . . . I see. Well, you might ask him as soon as he comes in if he could spare me a minute or two. It's urgent. Right.'

He hung up again, feeling a little better. If Sir Herbert could have words with the Commissioner, so could he. The old man could be a devil, but he wouldn't stand for his subordinates being humiliated, insulted and – yes, that was the word – blackmailed by pettifogging politicians. Meanwhile, however, this precious Dr Czissar wanted to talk about the Brock Park case. Right! Let him! He wouldn't be able to pull *that* to pieces. It was absolutely watertight. He picked up the file on the case. Yes, absolutely watertight.

Three years previously Thomas Medley, a widower of sixty with two adult children, had married Helena Murlin, a woman of forty-two. The four had since lived together in a large house in the London suburb of Brock Park. Medley, who had amassed a comfortable fortune on the Baltic Exchange, had retired from business shortly before his second marriage and had devoted most of his time since to his hobby, gardening. Helena Murlin was an artist, a landscape painter, and in Brock Park it was whispered that her pictures sold for large sums. She dressed both fashionably and smartly, and was disliked by her neighbours. Harold Medley, the son, aged twenty-five, was a medical student at a London hospital. His sister, Janet, was three years younger, and as dowdy as her stepmother was smart.

In the early October of that year, and as a result of an extra-heavy meal, Thomas Medley had retired to bed with a bilious attack. Such attacks had not been unusual. He had had an enlarged liver and had been normally dyspeptic. His doctor had prescribed in the usual way. On his third day in bed the patient had been considerably better. On the fourth day, however, at about four in the afternoon, he had been seized with violent abdominal pains, persistent vomiting, and severe cramps in the muscles of his legs.

These symptoms had persisted for three days, on the last of which there had been tetanic convulsions. He had died that night. The doctor had certified the death as being due to gastroenteritis. The dead man's estate had amounted to roughly £110,000. Half of it went to his wife. The remainder was divided equally between his two children.

A week after the funeral the police had received an anonymous letter suggesting that Medley had been poisoned. Subsequently they had received two further letters. Information had then reached them that several residents in Brock Park had received similar letters and that the matter was the subject of gossip. Medley's doctor had been approached later. He had reasserted that the death had been due to gastroenteritis, but confessed that the possibility of the condition having been brought about by the wilful administration of poison had not occurred to him. The body had been exhumed by licence of the Home Secretary and an autopsy performed. No traces of poison had been found in the stomach; but in the liver, kidneys, and spleen a total of 1.751 grains of arsenic had been found.

Inquiries had established that on the day on which the poisoning symptoms had appeared, the deceased had had a small luncheon consisting of breast of chicken, spinach (tinned), and one potato.

The cook had partaken of spinach from the same tin without suffering any ill effects. After his luncheon, Medley had taken a dose of the medicine prescribed for him by the doctor. It had been mixed with water for him by his son, Harold.

Evidence had been obtained from a servant that, a fortnight before the death, Harold had asked his father for £100 to settle a racing debt. He had been refused. Inquiries had revealed that Harold had lied. He had been secretly married for nearly six months, and the money had been needed not to pay racing debts, but for his wife, who was about to have a child.

The case against Harold had been conclusive. He had needed money desperately. He had quarrelled with his father. He had known that he was the heir to a quarter of his father's estate. As a medical student in a hospital, he had been in a position to obtain arsenic. The time at which symptoms of poisoning had appeared had shown that the arsenic must have been administered at about the time the medicine had been taken. It had been the first occasion on which Harold had prepared his father's medicine.

The coroner's jury had boggled at indicting him in their verdict, but he had later been arrested and was now on remand.

Mercer sat back in his chair. A watertight case. Sentences began to form in his mind. 'This Dr Czissar, Sir Charles, is merely a time-wasting crank. He's a refugee, and his sufferings have probably unhinged him a little. If you could put the matter to Sir Herbert . . .'

And then, for the second time that afternoon Dr Czissar was announced.

48

Mercer, as it will have been noted, was an angry man that afternoon. Yet, as Dr Czissar came into the room, he became conscious of a curious feeling of friendliness towards him. It was not entirely the friendliness that one feels towards an enemy one is about to destroy. In his mind's eye he had been picturing Dr Czissar as an ogre. Now Mercer saw that, with his cow-like eyes behind their thick pebble spectacles, his round, pale face, his drab grey raincoat, and his unfurled umbrella, Dr Czissar was, after all, merely pathetic. When, just inside the door, Dr Czissar stopped, clapped his umbrella to his side as if it were a rifle, and said loudly: 'Dr Jan Czissar. Late Prague police. At your service,' Mercer very nearly smiled.

Instead he said: 'Sit down, Doctor. I'm sorry I was too busy to see you earlier.'

'It is so good of you – ' began Dr Czissar earnestly.

'Not at all, Doctor. You want, I hear, to compliment us on our handling of the Brock Park case.'

Dr Czissar blinked. 'Oh, no, Assistant-Commissioner Mercer,' he said anxiously. 'I should like to compliment, but it is too early, I think. I do not wish to seem impolite, but . . .'

Mercer smiled complacently. 'Oh, we shall convict our man all right, Doctor. I don't think you need worry.'

'Oh, but I do worry. You see – he is not guilty.'

Mercer hoped that the smile with which he greeted the statement did not reveal his secret exultation. He said blandly, 'Are you aware, Doctor, of all the evidence?'

'I attended the inquest,' said Dr Czissar mournfully. 'But there will be more evidence from the hospital, no doubt. This Mr Harold could have stolen enough arsenic to poison a regiment without the loss being discovered.'

The fact that the words had been taken out of his mouth disconcerted Mercer only slightly. He nodded.

A faint, thin smile stretched the Doctor's full lips. He settled his glasses on his nose. Then he cleared his throat, swallowed hard, and leaned forward. 'Attention, please!' he said sharply.

For some reason that he could not fathom, Mercer felt his self-confidence ooze suddenly away. He had seen that same series of actions, ending with the peremptory demand for attention, performed once before, and it had been the prelude to disaster, to humiliation, to . . . He pulled himself up sharply. The Brock Park case was watertight.

'I'm listening,' he said irritably.

'Good.' Dr Czissar wagged one solemn finger. 'According to the medical evidence given at the inquest, arsenic was found in the liver, kidneys, and spleen. No?'

Mercer nodded firmly. '1.751 grains. That shows that much more than a fatal dose had been administered. Much more.'

Dr Czissar's eyes gleamed. 'Ah, yes. Much more. It is odd, is it not, that so much was found in the kidneys?'

'Nothing odd at all about it.'

'Let us leave the point for the moment. Is it not true, Assistant-Commissioner Mercer, that all post-mortem tests for arsenic are for arsenic itself and not for any particular arsenic salt?'

Mercer frowned. 'Yes, but it's unimportant. All arsenic salts are deadly poisons. Besides, when arsenic is absorbed by the human body, it turns to the sulphide. I don't see what you're driving at, Doctor.'

'My point is, Assistant-Commissioner, that usually it is impossible to tell from a delayed autopsy which form of arsenic was used to poison the body. You agree? It might be arsenious oxide or one of the arsenates or arsenites; copper arsenite, for instance; or it might be a chloride or it might be an organic compound of arsenic. No?'

'Precisely.'

'But,' continued Dr Czissar, 'what sort of arsenic should we expect to find in a hospital, eh?'

Mercer pursed his lips. 'I see no harm in telling you, Doctor, that Harold Medley could easily have secured supplies of either salvarsan or neosalvarsan. They are both important drugs.'

'Ehrlich's 606 and 914! Yes, indeed!' said Dr Czissar. He stared at the ceiling. 'Have you seen any of Helena Murlin's paintings, Assistant-Commissioner?'

The sudden change of subject took Mercer unawares. He hesitated. Then: 'Oh, you mean Mrs Medley. No, I haven't seen any of her paintings.'

'Such a *chic*, attractive woman,' said Dr Czissar. 'After I had seen her at the inquest I could not help wishing to see some of her work. I found some in a gallery near Bond Street.' He sighed. 'I had expected something clever, but I was disappointed. She is one of those who paint what they think instead of what is.'

'Really? I'm afraid, Dctor, that I must – '

'I felt,' persisted Dr Czissar, bringing his cow-like eyes once more to the level of Mercer's, 'that the thoughts of a woman who thinks of a field as blue and of a sky as emerald green must be a little strange.'

'Modern stuff, eh?' said Mercer. 'And now, Doctor, if you've finished, I'll ask you to excuse me. I – '

'Oh, but I have not finished yet,' said Dr Czissar kindly. 'I think, Assistant-Commissioner, that a woman who paints a landscape with a green sky is not only strange but also interesting, don't you? I asked the gentleman at the gallery about her. She produces only a few pictures – about six a year. She earns, perhaps, £100 a year from her work. It is wonderful how expensively she dresses on that sum.'

'She had a rich husband.'

'Oh, yes. A curious household, don't you think? The daughter Janet is especially curious. I was so sorry that she was so much upset by the evidence at the inquest.'

'A young woman probably would be upset at the idea of her brother's being a murderer,' said Mercer drily.

'But to accuse herself so violently of the murder.'

'Hysteria. You get a lot of it in murder cases.' Mercer stood up and held out his hand. 'Well, Doctor, I'm sorry you haven't been able to upset our case this time. If you'll leave your address with the Sergeant as you go, I'll see that you get a pass for the trial,' he added with relish.

But Dr Czissar did not move. 'You are going to try this young man for murder, then?' he said slowly. 'You have not understood that at which I have been hinting?'

Mercer grinned. 'We've got something better than hints, Doctor – a first-class circumstantial case against young Medley. Motive, time and method of administration, source of the poison. Concrete evidence, Doctor! Juries like it. If you can produce one scrap of evidence to show that we've got the wrong man, I'll be glad to hear it.'

Dr Czissar's back straightened and his cow-like eyes flashed.

'I do not like your condescension, Assistant-Commissioner!' he said sharply. 'I, too, am busy. I am engaged on a work on medical jurisprudence. I desire only to see justice done. I do not believe that, on the evidence you have, you can convict this young man under English law; but the fact of his being brought to trial could damage his career as a doctor. Furthermore, there is the real murderer to be considered. Therefore, in a spirit of friendliness, I have come to you instead of going to Harold Medley's legal advisers. I will now give you your evidence.'

Mercer sat down again. He was very angry.

'Attention, please,' said Dr Czissar. He raised a finger. 'Arsenic was found in the dead man's kidneys. It is determined that Harold Medley could have poisoned his father with either salvarsan or neosalvarsan. There is a contradiction there. Most inorganic salts of arsenic – white arsenic, for instance – are practically insoluble in water, and if a quantity of such a salt had been administered, we might expect to find traces of it in the kidneys. Salvarsan and neosalvarsan, however, are trivalent organic compounds of arsenic, and are very soluble in water. If either of them had been administered through the mouth, we should not expect to find arsenic in the kidneys.'

He paused; but Mercer was silent.

'In what form, therefore, was the arsenic administered?' he went on. 'The tests do not tell us, for they detect only the presence of the element, arsenic. That arsenic will also by that time be present as a sulphide. Let us look among the inorganic salts. There is white arsenic; that is arsenious oxide. It is used for dipping sheep. We should not expect to find it in Brock Park. But Mr Medley was a gardener. What about sodium arsenite, the weed-killer? We heard at the inquest that the weed-killer in the garden was of the kind harmful only to weeds. We come to copper arsenite. Mr Medley was, in my opinion, poisoned by a large dose of copper arsenite.'

'And on what evidence,' demanded Mercer, 'do you base that opinion?'

'There is, or there has been, copper arsenite in the Medleys' house.' Dr Czissar looked at the ceiling. 'On the day of the inquest, Assistant-Commissioner, Mrs Medley wore a fur coat. I have since found another fur coat like it. The price of the coat was 400 guineas. Inquiries in Brock Park have told me that this lady's husband, besides being a rich man, was also a very mean and unpleasant man. At the inquest his son told us that he had kept his marriage a secret because he was afraid that his father would stop his allowance or prevent his continuing his studies in medicine. Helena Murlin had expensive tastes. She had married this man so that she could indulge them. He had failed her. That coat she wore, Assistant-Commissioner, was unpaid for. You will find, I think, that she had other debts and that a threat had been made by one of the creditors to approach her husband. She was tired of this man, so much older than she was. Perhaps she had a young lover with no money to spend on her. But you will find these things out. She poisoned her husband. There is no doubt.'

'Nonsense!' snarled Mercer. 'Of course, we know that she was in debt, but lots of women are. It doesn't make them murderers.'

Dr Czissar smiled gently. 'It was the spinach which the dead man had for luncheon before the symptoms of poisoning began that interested me,' he said. 'Why give spinach when it is out of season? Tinned vegetables are not usually given to an invalid with gastric trouble. And then, when I saw Mrs Medley's paintings, I understood. The emerald sky, Assistant-Commissioner. It was a fine, rich emerald green, that sky – the sort of emerald green that the artist gets when there is aceto-arsenite of copper in the paint. The firm which supplies Mrs Medley with her working materials will be able to tell you when she bought it. I suggest, too, that you take the picture – it is in the Summons Gallery – and remove a little of the sky for analysis. As to the administration, you will find that the spinach was prepared at her suggestion and taken to her husband's bedroom by her. Spinach is green and slightly bitter in taste. So is copper arsenite.' He sighed. 'If there had not been anonymous letters –'

'Ah!' interrupted Mercer. 'The anonymous letters! Perhaps you know –'

'Oh, yes,' said Dr Czissar simply. 'The daughter, Janet, wrote them. Poor child! She disliked her smart stepmother, and wrote them out of spite. Imagine her feelings when she found that she had – how do you say? – put a noose about her brother's throat. It would be natural for her to try to take the blame herself. Good afternoon, and thank you,' he added.

'Good afternoon,' said Mercer wearily. The telephone rang. 'The Commissioner to speak to you, Sir,' said the operator.

'All right. Hullo . . . Hullo, Sir Charles. Yes, I did want to speak to you urgently. It was' – he hesitated – 'it was about the Brock Park case. I think that we shall have to release young Medley. I've got hold of some new medical evidence that – All right, Sir Charles, I'll come immediately.'

The Case of the Cycling Chauffeur

IT was generally felt by his subordinates at Scotland Yard that the best time to see Assistant-Commissioner Mercer was while he was drinking his afternoon tea. It was at teatime, therefore, that Detective-Inspector Denton took care to present a verbal report on the Mortons Hind case.

The village of Mortons Hind, Denton reported, was five miles from the market town of Penborough. Near the corner of the Penborough and Leicester roads, and about half a mile from the village, stood Mortons Grange, now the home of Mr Maurice Wretford, a retired City man, and his wife.

At half past three in the afternoon of November 10, Mr Wretford's chauffeur, Alfred Gregory, forty, had left the Grange to drive his employer's car to a Penborough garage, which was to hammer out and repaint a buckled wing. The job could not have been finished that day, and Gregory had taken his bicycle with him in the back of the car so that he could ride home. He had never returned to the Grange. At half past five that evening a motorist driving along a deserted stretch of road about a mile from the Grange had seen the bicycle lying in a ditch, and stopped. A few yards away, also in the ditch and dead, had been Gregory. He had a bullet in his head.

The lead bullet, which was of .22 calibre, had entered the left temple, leaving a small, circular wound halfway between the ear and the eye, torn through the brain tissue, and come to rest within half an inch of the upper surface of the left brain and immediately over the shattered sphenoid. There had been two small fractures of the skull extending from the puncture in the temporal bone, but no sign of scorching or powder-marks. This, and the fact that the diameter of the wound had been

55

less than the diameter of the bullet, had suggested that the shot had been fired at a distance of over six feet from the dead man's head.

The news of the shooting had spread quickly round the village, and late that night a gamekeeper, Harry Rudder, fifty-two, had reported to the police that that same afternoon he had seen a nineteen-year-old youth, Thomas Wilder, shooting at birds with a rook rifle not far from the spot where Gregory's body had been found. Wilder had admitted that he had been firing the rifle the previous day, but denied that he had been near the Penborough road. His rifle had been examined and found to be of .22 calibre.

It had not been until later that day that the post-mortem findings given above had been made known to the police. The fatal bullet had been handed to them at the same time. To their disgust, it had been badly distorted by its impact against the bones of the head. Any identification of rifling-marks had thus been rendered impossible. The bullet might have been fired from any .22 calibre weapon. Nevertheless, there had been a circumstantial case of manslaughter against Wilder to be considered. The Chief Constable of the County had decided to enlist the help of the ballistics experts of Scotland Yard.

The coroner had sat with a jury at the inquest. Gregory had had no living relatives. His employer, Mr Wretford, had given woebegone evidence of identification. The ballistics expert, Sergeant Blundell, had later given evidence. The bullet had been fired some distance from the deceased and at a level slightly below that of his head. The witness had agreed that a shot, fired from a rifle held to the shoulder of a man six feet in height (Wilder's height was six feet) standing in the meadow to the left of the road, at a bird in the tree on the opposite side of the road, could hit a passing cyclist in the head. The jury returned a verdict of 'Accidental death caused by the criminal negligence of Thomas Wilder'. Young Wilder had been arrested.

Mercer stirred his second cup of tea rather irritably. 'Yes, yes. All quite straightforward, isn't it? It's Blundell's show now. Send in your report in the usual way.'

'Yes, Sir – that is to say . . .' And then, to Mercer's amazement, Denton began to blush. 'It's straightforward all right, Sir. But' – he hesitated – 'but all the same . . .'

'All the same, what?' demanded Mercer.

Denton drew a deep breath. Then: 'All the same, Sir, I don't think Wilder's guilty, Sir,' he said.

Mercer's frown deepened. 'You don't, eh? Why? Come on, Denton, I haven't got all day to waste.'

Denton squirmed on his chair. 'Well, Sir, it isn't really my idea at all. It was that Czech refugee who was in the Prague police, that Dr Czissar.'

'Who did you say?' asked Mercer ominously.

Denton recognized the tone of voice and blundered on hurriedly. 'Dr Czissar, Sir. He was at the inquest. He spoke to me afterwards and, seeing that he was a friend of Sir Herbert at the Home Office, I thought I'd better humour him. He . . .'

But Mercer was scarcely listening. He was seeing a vision: a vision of a plump, pale man with pebble glasses and cow-like brown eyes, of a man wearing a long grey raincoat and a soft hat too large for him, and carrying an unfurled umbrella; of this same man sitting on the chair now occupied by Denton and politely telling him, Mercer, how to do his job. Twice it had happened. Twice had Dr Czissar proved that he was right and that Scotland Yard was wrong. And now . . .

Mercer pulled himself together. 'All right, Denton. I know Dr Czissar. Get on.'

Denton drew another breath. 'Well, Sir, he oozed up to me after the inquest and asked me to give you his compliments. Then he asked me what I thought about the verdict.'

'And what did you think?'

'I didn't get a chance to say, Sir. He didn't wait for an answer. He just said, "Attention, please!" in that way of his and said that Wilder was innocent. All very polite, you know, Sir, but pretty straight.'

Mercer did know. Dr Czissar's politeness set his teeth on edge. 'I see. And did he tell you what the proof was, or did you discover it for yourself?'

'Neither, Sir.'

'But you said that you believe that Wilder is innocent.'

'I do, Sir.' Denton hesitated for a moment. 'It's that Dr Czissar, Sir. He gets under your skin. I don't mind saying that, after he'd spoken to me, I took Blundell back with me to have another look at the place where Gregory was found; but I couldn't see anything wrong and neither could Blundell. The hedge varies in height, and there's a bit of a dip in it just there. From the meadow you couldn't see a man on a bike coming until he was right on top of you. The tree's just opposite that dip in the hedge, too. It's a big elm and there's not another tree either side of it for a hundred yards. The whole thing looked as clear as daylight to me: the sort of accident that's bound to happen if you let lads of nineteen play about with guns. And yet . . .'

Mercer smiled dryly. 'I should forget Dr Czissar's little fancies if I were you, Denton. You must remember that he's a refugee. His experiences have probably unhinged him a little. Understandable, of course.'

'You mean he's dotty, Sir?' Denton considered the proposition. 'Well, he does look it a bit. But, begging your pardon, Sir, he wasn't so dotty about the Seabourne business. And there was that Brock Park case, too. If it hadn't been for him . . . You see, Sir, it's sort of worried me, him going on about Wilder being innocent.' He hesitated. 'He says he's coming in to see you this afternoon, Sir,' he concluded.

'Oh, does he!'

'Yes, Sir. About five.' Denton looked anxious. 'If you can let me know what he says, Sir, I'd be grateful.'

'All right, Denton. I'll let you know.'

Denton went out with the buoyant step and the revolting smile of one who realizes that he has handled a difficult situation with tact and resource. Mercer stared after him.

So, he reflected, it had come to this. His subordinates were hanging on the words of this precious Dr Czissar like – he cast about wildly for a simile – like schoolboys round a Test cricketer. It was worse than humiliating. It was demoralizing. Here was he, Assistant-Commissioner Mercer, sitting in his room waiting for an unemployed Czech policeman to teach him his job. Something would have to be done. But what? To refuse to see the man would be simply to invite trouble with that old fool at the Home Office. Besides – he wrung the confession from his subconscious mind with masochistic savagery – he *wanted* to see Dr Czissar, and not entirely in the hope of hearing the Czech make a fool of himself. He was – he admitted it bitterly – curious.

He was still staring helplessly at his untasted second cup of tea when Dr Czissar was announced.

Dr Czissar came into the room, clapped his umbrella to his side, clicked his heels, bowed and said: 'Dr Jan Czissar. Late Prague police. At your service.'

Mercer watched this all too familiar performance with unconcealed dislike. 'Sit down, Doctor,' he said shortly. 'Inspector Denton tells me that you wish to make a suggestion about the Mortons Hind case.'

Dr Czissar sat down carefully and leaned forward. 'Thank you, Assistant-Commissioner,' he said earnestly. 'It is so good of you to receive me again.'

Mercer strove to detect the note of mockery which he felt might be there. 'No trouble,' he returned gruffly.

Dr Czissar shook his head. 'You are so kind. Everyone is so kind. You see, Assistant-Commissioner, the thing which an exile misses most is his work. To me, police work is my life. I am grateful to you for the opportunities which you have given me, an intruder, to make myself of use again.'

'Very nice of you to put it that way,' Mercer said curtly. 'And now, if you've got something to tell me . . .'

Dr Czissar sat back quickly. Mercer could almost feel his disappointment. 'Of course, Assistant-Commissioner,' he said stiffly. 'I will not waste your time. If it had not been for the innocence of this boy Wilder, I would not have troubled you.'

Mercer cleared his throat. 'To me, the case seems perfectly straightforward. Our expert, Blundell . . .'

'Ah!' Dr Czissar's eyes gleamed. 'That is the word. Expert. The witness which the lawyers always attack, eh?'

Mercer gave him a wry smile. 'Our expert witnesses, Doctor, are practically lawyers themselves. They're used to cross-examination.'

'Precisely. Sergeant Blundell was obviously experienced. He answered honestly and sincerely just those questions which were put to him, *as* they were put to him. No more, no less. It is praiseworthy. Unfortunately, such testimony may be misleading.'

'What do you mean?'

'Sergeant Blundell was asked, Assistant-Commissioner, whether a shot fired from a rifle held to the shoulder of a man in the field to the left of the road at a bird in the tree on the right of the road could hit a passing cyclist and make a wound such as that found in Mr Gregory. He very properly answered that it could.'

'Well?'

Dr Czissar smiled faintly. 'Sergeant Blundell had taken measurements and made calculations. They were accurate. But he did not actually fire at any bird in that tree himself. His observations were therefore incomplete. His answer was legally correct. Mr Gregory *could* have been so killed. But he was *not* so killed. And for a simple reason. For Wilder to have fired the shot at that particular angle, the bird would have had to have been on a branch about eighteen feet from the ground. The lowest branch on that tree, Assistant-Commissioner, is about ten feet above that.'

Mercer sat up. 'Are you sure of that, Doctor?'

'I could not make a mistake about such a thing,' said Dr Czissar with dignity.

'No, no, of course not. Excuse me a moment, Doctor.' Mercer picked up the telephone. 'I want Inspector Denton and Sergeant Blundell to see me immediately.'

There was an embarrassed silence until they came. Then Dr Czissar was asked to repeat his statement. Denton snapped his fingers.

Mercer looked at Blundell. 'Well?'

Blundell reddened. 'It's possible, Sir. I can't say that I looked at the thing from that standpoint. Perhaps it was something on the trunk of the tree – a squirrel, perhaps.'

Denton grinned. 'I can answer that one, Sir. I was brought up in the country. You wouldn't find a squirrel climbing up the trunk of an odd elm tree by the side of a main road in November. That makes it murder, eh, Doctor?'

Dr Czissar frowned. 'That,' he said stiffly, 'is for the Assistant-Commissioner to decide, Inspector.' He turned courteously to Mercer. 'If you will permit me, Assistant-Commissioner, to make a further suggestion?'

Mercer nodded wearily. 'Go ahead, Doctor.'

A thin smile stretched the doctor's full lips. He settled his glasses on his nose. Then he cleared his throat, swallowed hard, and leaned forward. 'Attention, please,' he said sharply.

He had their attention.

'To you, Assistant-Commissioner Mercer,' began Dr Czissar, 'I would say that no blame in this matter belongs to Inspector Denton or Sergeant Blundell. They were obviously expected by the local police to prove a case of manslaughter against Wilder, and they contrived to do so. The case was spoilt for them before they arrived. This man Gregory was found shot. Either he was shot accidentally or he was murdered. A small community dislikes the thought of murder even more than a large one. But they do not have to think of murder, for here, under their noses, is a better explanation. Wilder was firing a .22 rifle. Gregory was killed with a .22 bullet. *Ergo*, Wilder killed Gregory. Everyone is happy – except Wilder and myself. I am not happy; especially when I see that the shooting could not have happened as is said. It seems to me that even though the local police dislike the idea, murder has been done. Who has done it? I begin, logically, with the victim.

'At the inquest,' resumed Dr Czissar, 'Mr Wretford, so sad at losing his good chauffeur, said that Gregory had been in his employ for three years, and that he was sober, steady, and of excellent character. And the poor man had no friends or relations living. Such a pity, and so unusual. I decided to investigate a little. I went to the garage at Penborough and talked to a mechanic there. I found that Mr Wretford had made a little mistake about his chauffeur. Gregory was not very sober. Also, he betted a great deal for a man in his position. The mechanic was able to tell me that he dealt with a bookmaker in Penborough. To this bookmaker I went.'

Dr Czissar looked suddenly embarrassed. 'I am afraid,' he said apologetically, 'that I have been guilty of an offence. You see, Assistant-Commissioner Mercer, I wished for information from this bookmaker. I said that I was from the police, without saying that it was the Prague police. I found that Gregory had, in the last twelve months, lost two hundred and thirty-seven pounds to this bookmaker.'

Mercer jumped. 'What!'

'Two hundred and thirty-seven pounds, Assistant-Commissioner. In addition, he had asked for no credit. He had received his winnings and paid his losses in pound notes. His wages, I think, could not have been sufficient to absorb such losses.'

'He earned two pounds a week and his keep, according to Wretford,' Denton put in.

'Ah, quite so.' Dr Czissar smiled gently. 'The bookmaker had concluded that the bets were really made by Mr Wretford, who did not wish, for personal reasons, to have it known that he betted. It seems that such reticences are not unusual. But Gregory had been murdered. That *was* unusual. The bookmaker's conclusion did not satisfy me. I made other inquiries. Among other things, I found that eight years ago, just before Mr Wretford retired, a clerk in his office was convicted of stealing the sum of fifteen thousand pounds in bearer bonds and three hundred pounds in cash. I was able to find a full report of the case in the newspaper files. The prosecution showed that he had got into debt through betting and that he had been systematically stealing small sums over a long period. The prosecution argued that, having gained confidence from the fact that his petty thefts went undiscovered, he had stolen the bearer bonds. There was one curious feature about the affair. The bearer bonds were not found and the prisoner refused to say anything about them except that he had stolen them. His sentence was, therefore, unusually severe for a first offender – five years' penal servitude. His name was Selton.'

'I remember the case,' said Denton eagerly. 'Gregory Selton – that was the name.'

'Precisely!' said Dr Czissar. '*Gregory*. A young man who right until his death, was too fond of betting. He must have changed his name when he came out of prison. Now, we find him in the last place we should expect to find him. He is Mr Wretford's chauffeur. Mr Wretford, the man he robbed of fifteen thousand pounds!'

Mercer shrugged. 'Generous gesture on Wretford's part. It doesn't explain why he was shot or who shot him.'

Dr Czissar smiled. 'Nor why Mr Wretford lied at the inquest?'

'What are you getting at?'

Dr Czissar held up a finger. 'Attention, please! The only logical part of that case against Selton was that he had over a long period stolen sums in cash amounting to three hundred pounds and intended to pay off racing debts. That is the thieving of a clerk. That he should suddenly steal fifteen

thousand pounds is absurd. And we only have his word for it
that he did steal them.'

'But why on earth should . . .?'

'Mr Wretford's reputation,' pursued Dr Czissar, 'was not
very good in the City. I believe that those bonds were converted by Mr Wretford for his own private profit, and that he
was in danger of being found out when he discovered Selton's
thefts. He was desperate, perhaps. Selton, he thought, would
go to prison, anyway. Let him agree to take a little extra blame
and all would be well. Selton would have his reward when he
came out of prison. Alas for Mr Wretford! Mr Gregory Selton
was not content with comfortable and overpaid employment.
He began, I think, to blackmail Mr Wretford. Those racing
debts, you see. More money, more money always. Mr Wretford was very wise to kill him under the circumstances.'

'But . . .'

'But, how? Ah, yes.' Dr Czissar smiled kindly upon them. 'It
was, I think, a sudden idea. The grounds of his house are
extensive. He probably heard Wilder using the rook rifle near
by and thought of his own rifle. He used to be a member of a
City rifle club. Selton would, he knew, be returning soon. It
would be possible for him to get from his house to that place
behind the hedge without going on to the road and risking
being seen. When Selton was found, the blame would be put on
this boy. For him, a few months in prison; for the respectable
Mr Wretford, safety. He stood behind the hedge at a range of
perhaps ten feet from Selton as he cycled by. It would have
been difficult to miss.'

Dr Czissar stood up. 'It is a suggestion only, of course,' he
said apologetically. 'You will be able to identify Selton from his
finger-prints and arrest Mr Wretford on a charge of perjury.
The rifle will no doubt be found when you search the Grange.
An examination of Mr Wretford's accounts will show that he was
being blackmailed by Selton. Those large sums in one pound
notes . . . but it is not for me to teach you your business, eh?'
He smiled incredulously at the idea. 'It is time for me to go.
Good evening, Assistant-Commissioner.'

For a moment there was a silence. Then:

'I knew there was something funny about this case, Sir,' said
Denton brightly. 'Clever chaps, these Czechs.'

The Case of the Overheated
Service Flat

ASSISTANT-COMMISSIONER Mercer did not often attend inquests. It was not part of his duty to do so. The fact that on that foggy December morning he should be sitting in a coroner's court in a London suburb instead of in his room at New Scotland Yard argued wholly exceptional circumstances.

The circumstances were indeed exceptional. It looked as though a murderer were going to escape the consequences of his crime and as if there were nothing that Scotland Yard could do about it.

In 1933 the wife of Mr Thomas Jones, an industrial chemist living in a Midland town, had died in her bath from carbon-monoxide poisoning. At the inquest her death had been found to be due to a defective geyser. Three months previously Mr Jones had insured her life for £5000; but although the police reviewed the possibility of his having engineered the defect in the geyser, no proof of his having done so had been forthcoming. A verdict of 'Accidental Death' had been returned.

In 1935 Mr Jones had married again. His second wife had been fifteen years his senior. It had been, no doubt, the £15,000 which the second Mrs Jones had inherited from her mother that had bridged the difference in their ages. But Mr Jones was, it seemed, unlucky in love. Eighteen months after their marriage the second Mrs Jones had died; and, strange to relate, from carbon-monoxide poisoning. She had been found in her car, which had been inside the garage with the engine running. According to the hapless Mr Jones, his wife had been subject to fainting fits. Evidently she had driven the car into the garage, felt faint, and remained in the driving-seat. There had been a strong wind and no doubt the garage doors had blown to,

64

leaving her at the mercy of the exhaust fumes. The fact that a small quantity of veronal had been found in her stomach had, to the irritation of the police, been accounted for by her doctor, who had said that she had been in the habit of taking sleeping draughts. A verdict of 'Accidental Death' had been returned.

In 1938 Mr Jones, now of independent means, had married yet again. His third wife's name had been Rose, and she had had an income of £1200 a year from freehold house property left to her by her father. The week before the inquest which Mercer was now attending Mrs Jones had died – from carbon-monoxide poisoning.

The couple had lived in a block of expensive service flats. According to a preternaturally lugubrious Mr Jones, he had been at his golf club on the afternoon of 'the tragedy' and had returned home at about six o'clock to find the flat full of coal-gas and his wife dead in her bed. The gas-fire in the bedroom had been turned full on. His wife, he said, had been of a 'sunny' disposition, and he could think of no reason why she should have 'taken her life'. In his opinion, propounded at length to the police inspector, she had been getting into bed for her afternoon nap, had caught the hem of her housecoat on the tap, and in freeing it had unwittingly turned the tap on. The fumes – here Mr Jones had exercised visible restraint over his emotions – had overcome her while she had been asleep.

Mercer listened to the evidence gloomily. With the facts about Mr Jones's earlier matrimonial adventures in mind, Mercer had no doubt that Rose Jones had been murdered. The difficulty was to prove it. The law, very rightly, prohibited any mention of the fate of Mr Jones's first two wives while the fate of the third was still *sub judice*. No doubt Mr Jones was aware of that. Mercer saw that the man was making an excellent impression on the jury. A demure figure in deep mourning, he was giving his evidence with sublime disregard of the implications contained in the questions being put to him.

Yes, he had given instructions for the gas-fire to be installed. No, it had been at his wife's request that he had done so. No, it was not strange that she should need a gas-fire in a centrally heated room. She had felt the cold. Yes, it was the only gas-fire in the flat. There was a portable electric radiator in another room, but his wife had not liked it in the bedroom.

No, it was not strange that he had insisted upon an old-type gas-fire instead of the new type with the tap built into the fire. His wife had expressed a preference for the former. He was sorry now that he had not insisted upon the new type. The accident could not then have happened.

He had left his wife at two thirty to go to his golf club, ten minutes' walk away. No, he had not gone straight there. He had gone first to a newsagent's shop and bought a fashion magazine for his wife. He had then returned to the entrance lobby to the flats and asked the hall porter to take the magazine up to Mrs Jones. He had then gone on to the golf club.

No, he had not seen his wife alive after leaving the flat at two thirty. The hall porter must have been the last person to see her alive. As far as he could remember, he had arrived at the golf club at about three o'clock. But he couldn't be certain. The secretary at the golf club would probably remember. He had met him soon after he had arrived.

Yes (this with a puzzled frown), there was a gas-meter in the flat. Yes, the main gas-tap was beside it. As far as he could remember, the meter was at the top of a cupboard just inside the door of the flat. Yes, he believed that he had suggested its installation there instead of in the kitchen. To have installed it in the kitchen would have meant loss of cupboard-space.

The jury, Mercer noted, were beginning to fidget. Clearly they did not see the point of this questioning. He scowled at them. The blockheads! They had been shown a plan of the flats. And didn't they ever read their newspapers? Couldn't they visualize the scene? Mr Jones turning the gas off at the main and then turning on the gas-fire in the bedroom; Mr Jones returning to the lobby with a magazine; the hall porter going up in the lift to deliver the magazine while Mr Jones ascended again by the stairs? Couldn't they see Mr Jones waiting on the stairs while the hall porter descended again and his wife got into bed? Couldn't they see Mr Jones quietly opening the door of the flat, reaching up to the cupboard, turning the main gas-tap on again, and quietly leaving? The hall porter had admitted that he didn't watch the entrance all the time. Didn't they see that Mr Jones could have done these things and got to his golf club in time to show himself to a doddering old fool of a secretary 'soon after' three? It must be obvious. 'Blockheads!' he muttered, and heard Detective-Inspector Denton beside him stir in sympathy.

And then he saw Dr Czissar.

The refugee Czech detective was sitting in one of the seats reserved for the Press and as his brown, cow-like eyes met Mercer's grey ones, he inclined his head respectfully.

Mercer nodded curtly and looked away. He heard Denton's grunt of surprise and hoped that his subordinate would not find it necessary to comment on Dr Czissar's presence at the inquest. The last person he wanted to think about at that moment was Dr Jan Czissar. Since the first day on which this pale, bespectacled Czech had walked into his office bearing an unfurled umbrella and a letter of introduction from a Home Office politician, Mercer had been nursing a badly wounded self-esteem. Twice had the wound been reopened. Three times in all had he had to listen to Dr Czissar demonstrating, with his infuriating lecture-room mannerisms, that Scotland Yard could be wrong while he, Dr Jan Czissar, 'late Prague police', was right.

Now, as he sat listening to a gas company official confirming Mr Jones's account of the installation of the gas-fire, Mercer tried to put Dr Czissar out of his mind. But his mind, nagged by the memories of past humiliations, refused to part with Dr Czissar. It began to speculate as to why Dr Czissar was there at the inquest, what he was doing in the Press seats, and what he was thinking about the case. It was with a heartfelt sigh of relief that he heard the coroner's announcement that the court would adjourn for the luncheon interval.

He stood up. 'We might get a drink and a sandwich across the road, Denton.'

'Right, Sir.'

They had gone about three paces before Nemesis, worming its way between a policeman and a stout member of the general public, overtook them.

'Assistant-Commissioner Mercer, please,' said Dr Czissar breathlessly, 'Dr Jan Czissar. Late Prague police. At your service. I should like, if you please, to speak about this case.' He bowed quickly to Denton.

Mercer gave him a rancid smile. 'Ah, Dr Czissar! Are you working for the Press now, Doctor?'

Dr Czissar hesitated. 'The Press? No, I am still working on my book on medical jurisprudence. Ah, I see. The seat. It was lent to me by a journalist with a Press card. But' – he smiled shyly – 'perhaps I should not say that, eh?'

Mercer grunted. The Doctor, his long, grey raincoat flapping about his legs, was now loping along beside them. Denton, who, with less dignity to lose than Mercer, thought Dr Czissar very clever indeed, would have liked to have discussed the case, but seeing Mercer's face, kept silent.

'I was very surprised,' pursued Dr Czissar as they descended the steps to the street, 'to see you in this court this morning, Assistant-Commissioner. It appeared such an unimportant case. But then, of course, I had not heard the evidence. I wish to compliment you, Assistant-Commissioner. It was so clever, I thought, the way in which the existence of the electric radiator was established. I was afraid for a time that the murderer's trick was going to succeed. But I should have known better. It is a most interesting case.'

But Mercer had stopped dead. 'What did you say about an electric radiator?' he demanded.

Dr Czissar looked a little scared as he repeated the sentence.

'May I remind you, Doctor,' snapped Mercer, 'that Mrs Jones was not burnt to death or electrocuted, but gassed?'

A puzzled look came over the Doctor's face. 'But I thought,' he said hesitantly, 'that you understood . . .' He did not finish the sentence. The puzzled look on his face gave way to one of acute embarrassment. He drew himself up. 'I beg your pardon, Assistant-Commissioner,' he said formally. 'I have made a mistake. If you will excuse me, please?'

At that moment something inside Mercer's stomach seemed to drop about six inches, and in the fraction of a second which it took to do so, he realized that his humiliations at the hands of Dr Czissar were not ended; that the wound was to be opened yet again. There was nothing else for it. Dr Czissar had obviously understood something about the case that he had not understood. He, Mercer, must know what that something was before the inquest ended in a verdict of 'Accidental Death'. And there was only one way of finding out. He steeled himself for the ordeal. Then:

'I should very much like to discuss the case with you, Doctor,' he said ceremoniously. 'Inspector Denton and I were about to take a little refreshment. If you would care to accompany us . . .'

Three minutes later a thoroughly bewildered Dr Czissar was sitting with a whisky and soda and a ham sandwich in front of him. 'It is most kind of you, Assistant-Commissioner,' he was repeating over and over again. The brown eyes behind the thick pebble glasses were almost tearful.

'Not at all.' Mercer took a deep breath. 'I have a confession to make to you, Doctor. We do not *know* that this is a case of murder. We only *believe* so. Jones has had three wives, of which this woman was the third. All have died apparently accidental deaths from carbon-monoxide poisoning. All three deaths have been of financial benefit to Jones. That is the basis of our belief that Jones is a murderer. But from the evidence at our disposal we are frankly unable to prove it. In our opinion, as you will have gathered from the questions asked this morning, Jones returned to the flat before he went to the golf club and turned on the main gas-tap so that the gas escaped into his wife's room while she was asleep. All he would have to do before he went out would be to leave the fire tap on and the main tap off. But it is proof we need. Now, Doctor, you've helped us before. If you can help us again we shall be obliged.'

Dr Czissar's pleasure was, Denton thought, pathetic. 'Assistant-Commissioner Mercer,' he said eagerly, 'I am profoundly honoured by your confidence. It is a great joy to me to be able to help the nation which has shown such hospitality to me and others of my unhappy countrymen. I, too, will be frank. But for your presence in court I should have stopped to hear no more than the medical evidence. Now I will tell you this. If I had known what you have now told me about Mr Jones, I do not think that I should have understood this case. He is a very clever man. I will explain to you why.'

'Please do,' said Mercer drily.

A faint, thin smile stretched the Doctor's full lips. He settled his spectacles on his nose. Then he cleared his throat, swallowed hard, and leaned forward. 'Attention, please!' he said sharply.

'In the first place,' said Dr Czissar, 'I considered this story of the gas-fire being turned on accidentally. I tried to think of it actually happening. There is a tap, and this lady has a long coat which catches in the tap, turning it on. So far it is possible. Improbable, as are all accidents, but possible. What happens now? According to Mr Jones's evidence, the tap was turned full on when he returned to the flat and found his wife dead. Therefore we are asked to believe that while the lady was taking off her coat, getting into bed and going to sleep, the tap was all the time turned fully on. That, I thought, was not possible. Assistant-Commissioner, I will explain why.'

'We'll accept the proposition,' put in Mercer hastily.

'To begin with,' persisted Dr Czissar, 'a gas-fire turned full on and unlighted makes a little noise. But let us assume that this lady was a little deaf. There is now the *smell* of the gas to be considered. My own sense of smell is not particularly sensitive, but I can easily detect one part of coal-gas in seven hundred parts of air. Many persons – especially those who do not smoke – can detect by smell one part in ten thousand. Is it credible that this lady should be awake in a small room for several minutes with the gas-fire turned full on without smelling it? I think not!'

'The accident, then, is impossible. And is not the police theory also impossible? Mr Jones leaves the flat at half past two. At two thirty-five he hands the magazine to the hall porter. He then has to go up the stairs and wait until the porter has gone and his wife is asleep. Let us assume that he knows his wife's habits very well and that he can be sure when she will go to sleep. He will have to wait on the stairs at least twenty minutes. Then he has to leave the building and reach the golf club without being seen. The risk to him would have been enormous. He might have been seen on the stairs by one of the other tenants. I cannot believe that a man like Mr Jones would have taken such a risk.'

'Then it wasn't murder?' said Denton.

Dr Czissar smiled. 'Oh, yes, it was murder, Inspector. There is no doubt of it. But consider Mr Jones's cleverness. He planned to murder his third wife. Very well. He realized at once that however skilfully he made it look like an accident, the police would suspect murder because of the first two cases you mention to me. Here is his cleverness: he decides to use your suspicions to make himself quite safe from conviction. You

70

believed, naturally, that he stole back and turned on the main tap. Think how much he helped you to that belief! He had the gas-fire installed in spite of the fact that there was efficient steam-heating in the room. Very suspicious. He asked specially for an obsolete type of fire, which would enable him to say that the affair was accidental. Very suspicious. His alibi is not perfect. Again suspicious. The only thing he did not help you to was the *proof* that he returned to the flat. And he knows that you cannot get it for yourselves. Why? Because it does not exist. He did *not* return to the flat. He is therefore safe. What does it matter to him if he is suspect? You cannot prove anything against him, because you are trying to prove something that did not happen.'

'Blimey!' said Denton.

'Blind you, indeed!' agreed Dr Czissar courteously. 'For me, however, things were different. I did not know of these other murders. I saw only the facts of this case. I saw only a woman poisoned by carbon-monoxide and a man who has been an industrial chemist inheriting a fortune. Coal-gas? So *he* says. But he is suspect.'

'But, dammit – !' began Mercer explosively.

'Coal-gas,' pursued Dr Czissar, 'is undoubtedly poisonous because of the carbon-monoxide contained in it. But for an industrial chemist there would be other ways of filling a room with carbon-monoxide. A small charcoal brazier, for instance.'

'There was,' said Mercer, 'no charcoal brazier in the flat.'

'Nor any sign of one,' added Denton.

Dr Czissar giggled. 'Dear me, no. I did not expect that there was. I give you only an example. But did you notice, Assistant-Commissioner, that although much was made of the strangeness of the gas-fire in a steam-heated flat, no one found it strange that there should also be an electric radiator there.'

'You mean he put charcoal on the electric radiator?'

'No, please.' Dr Czissar raised a finger admonishingly. 'I did not say that. The man is a chemist. What is the laboratory method of preparing pure carbon-monoxide? I will tell you. One reduces chalk by heating it with zinc dust. He would not need much. One part of carbon-monoxide in one hundred parts of air is a sufficient concentration to kill in a very short time –

little more than an hour. And pure carbon-monoxide has *no* smell.'

'But –'

'Attention, please!' said Dr Czissar sharply. 'I think the murder was done this way. Before he went out that day, Mr Jones took the radiator and put it on its back underneath his wife's bed. He then sprinkled the heater elements all over with the mixture of chalk and zinc dust, and, having plugged the radiator into the power point, said goodbye. Next, he sent the hall porter up with the magazine to establish that his wife was alive when he left. But she was not alive for long. When the radiator became hot, the chalk and zinc dust reacted together and produced large quantities of carbon-monoxide. When he returned home at six o'clock she was dead. He then removed the radiator and turned on the gas-fire. When the flat smelled strongly of coal-gas he summoned help.'

'But the proof, man – the proof!'

'Oh, yes. The zinc dust would have to be purchased from a laboratory supplier. It is much used as a reducing agent. Examination of the radiator will be helpful also. Your chemist will be able to find traces of both calcium and zinc oxides on the elements. And it is probable that the carpet under the bed will be scorched. Even the backs of radiators get very hot.'

Mercer looked at Denton. 'Better ask the coroner for an adjournment, hadn't we, Sir?'

Mercer nodded. Then he looked again at Dr Czissar, who was nibbling his sandwich.

'Well, Doctor,' he said as heartily as he could, 'we've got to thank you once again.' He raised his glass. 'Here's to you!'

Dr Czissar dropped his sandwich. His pale cheeks flushed slightly. He beamed with pleasure.

'I have not yet tasted English whisky,' he said quickly, 'but I know the English toast.' He raised his glass. 'Cheerio! All the best!' he said in ringing tones.

He drank, put the glass down, and shuddered violently.

'All the best,' he repeated bravely, and took a large bite out of the sandwich.

The Case of the Drunken Socrates

THERE are at New Scotland Yard patient, disillusioned men whose business it is to examine the work of England's great army of anonymous letter-writers. They read, they classify, they file. One letter in a thousand may possibly be worth more than momentary consideration. Assistant-Commissioner Mercer can scarcely be blamed for the attitude which he adopted towards the affair which the newspapers later called 'the drunken Socrates case'.

Yet it must be admitted that, even had there been no question of anonymous letters, Mercer would have disliked the case from the beginning. The reason is simple. The case was brought to his notice by Dr Jan Czissar.

A wound to his self-esteem is unpleasant enough even for an ordinary man. For an Assistant-Commissioner at Scotland Yard it is positively demoralizing. And when it is considered that Dr Czissar had inflicted on him not one such wound, but four, Mercer must be excused. On four separate occasions had Dr Czissar been able to prove, politely but irrefutably, that Scotland Yard in general and Assistant-Commissioner Mercer in particular were not infallible; and, though a simple soul might expect Mercer to be grateful, he was not.

It so happened that on the December afternoon on which Dr Czissar chose to intrude for the fifth time into the affairs of Scotland Yard, Mercer was feeling pleased with himself. He had just brought a difficult case to a triumphant conclusion. The Commissioner had congratulated him. The very existence of Dr Czissar had been forgotten. He felt strong and capable.

And then Dr Czissar was announced.

Wounds to the self-esteem do not heal easily; not even when they are forgotten. If Mercer was surprised and annoyed by the sudden tightening inside his chest which was the immediate result of the announcement, he was infuriated by the behaviour of his mind. Before he realized it, his mind was passing in quick review the various cases on which his department was working at the moment and wondering which of them was about to receive the disruptive attention of Dr Czissar. He pulled himself together savagely. He was losing his sense of proportion.

'All right,' he said wearily. 'I'll see him.'

A minute later he heard the flapping of Dr Czissar's long drab raincoat echoing along the corridor outside and waited, like a prisoner awaiting the next turn of the thumb-screw, for Dr Czissar's inevitable greeting. It came. The Doctor walked into the room, halted, clapped his unfurled umbrella to his side, clicked his heels, and intoned loudly: 'Dr Jan Czissar. Late Prague police. At your service!'

'How are you, Doctor? Please take a seat.'

The round, pale face relaxed. The brown, cow-like eyes enlarged behind the thick pebble spectacles.

'I am well, thank you, Assistant-Commissioner Mercer.' He sat down. 'Quite well, but a little worried. Otherwise I would not take your time. It is about a very curious case.'

Mercer steeled himself. 'Yes?' He laughed with ghastly jocularity. 'What has the Yard done this time, Doctor? Let another murderer slip through its fingers?'

Dr Czissar looked shocked. 'Oh, no, please. I think that that is most unlikely. Everything is most efficient here. There is, I think, a murder to be considered but I do not think that Scotland Yard has failed. The police do not know of this case. I must explain that it is only because of my landlady that I know of it.'

'Your landlady?'

'I live, Assistant-Commissioner, in Metternich Square, in Bloomsbury. It is a very nice house. Very clean, and there are only four other lodgers – students at the University. It is owned by my landlady, Mrs Falcon. It is this lady who, knowing that I have some experience in police matters, brought the matter to me for my advice.' The cow-like eyes became more pathetic. 'And so now, Assistant-Commissioner Mercer, I bring it to *you* for advice, if you will be so kind.'

Advice! Dr Czissar was asking *him* for advice! Mercer could scarcely believe his ears.

'Of course, Doctor. Anything we can do.'

'You are so kind. May I tell you about this case?'

'Yes. Please do.'

'It begins,' said Dr Czissar solemnly, 'with a death. On 20 June of this year my landlady's brother, Captain Pewsey, died suddenly at his house in Meresham, which is a town twenty miles from London. It was a very distressing thing for my landlady, who was very fond of her brother, in spite of his faults. You see, Assistant-Commissioner, he drank too much whisky. About five years ago he married a woman much younger than he was. Mrs Falcon thinks that this Mrs Pewsey did not make him happy.

'I have said that the Captain drank a lot. About a week before his death he went to a doctor in Meresham and complained of his heart. The doctor examined him and found a little cardiac weakness. He advised the Captain to drink less whisky and to live carefully. There was no great danger, he said, but it would be as well if the Captain avoided excesses.

'For several days after that visit to the doctor the Captain drank less whisky, but on the night of 20 June he spent the evening with a friend – Mr Stenson.

'The Captain was in the business of selling life insurance policies, and he had met Mr Stenson through selling him a policy. The friendship continued through the game of golf. There was, perhaps, a financial reason for the Captain's liking for Mr Stenson: Mr Stenson works in the City of London and he has made much money and knows important persons. The Captain would have found him useful.

'The first part of that evening of the 20th the Captain spent with Mr Stenson and other men at the golf club; but at about ten o'clock the Captain and Mr Stenson left the club together and walked towards their houses. Mr Stenson's house was reached first and the Captain went in with him to drink more whisky. Soon after eleven o'clock the Captain left and went to his own house. It seems that he was then a little drunk. His wife had already gone to bed, and she said afterwards that she heard him stumble along the passage to his room. Then she went to sleep. In the morning, when she went into his room, she found him

75

sitting in an armchair still dressed. He was very blue in the face and seemed dead.

'She called the doctor immediately. He came and found that the Captain was indeed dead. The doctor was a little puzzled. He had examined the Captain a week before, but he had not thought that his heart was in so bad a state that a little too much whisky would kill him. He told these things to Mrs Pewsey and said that before signing the death certificate he would ask her permission to make a post-mortem examination. She was reluctant, but as he insisted, she agreed. He made the examination, found that the death had been due to a respiratory failure, and concluding that the cause of it had been the weakness of the heart, issued a certificate to that effect.'

'A very cautious doctor,' commented Mercer.

Dr Czissar's cow-like eyes contemplated his. 'Doctors should always be cautious, I think. But I will continue with the story. A month ago Mr Stenson married Mrs Pewsey.'

Mercer raised his eyebrows. 'Quick work!'

Dr Czissar nodded sadly. 'That is what Mrs Falcon thought. She heard about the marriage from a friend who lives at Meresham. She was most upset. She had rarely seen her brother since his marriage, as she did not like Mrs. Pewsey; but her affection for him remained. She thought it unpleasant that his widow should have shown so little respect for his memory. It was also a surprise to her, for she had heard nothing of any friendship between the two at the funeral. And then' – he delved into his pocket and produced three folded sheets of notepaper – 'Mrs Falcon showed these to me. There are three of them, and they are marked in order.'

Mercer took the sheets and selected Number One.

Dear Mrs Falcon [he read] –
Your sister-in-law has married your brother's friend. So soon! Strange, is it not? I should ask a few questions if I were you. Why did your brother die? He was in the prime of life. He had the best years before him. Doctors don't know everything. Captain Pewsey was as strong as an ox. – Yours truly, A FRIEND.

It was typewritten. He glanced quickly at the remaining letters, saw that they were similar and looked up.

'Well, Doctor? We get plenty of this sort of thing here. Do you know who wrote them?'

Dr Czissar nodded. 'Oh, yes. Mrs Falcon wrote them.'

'To herself!'

'Yes. She said that she had thrown the envelopes away. Also' – Dr Czissar smiled sadly – 'there are phrases there of which Mrs Falcon is very fond. Mrs Falcon is a kind woman, but she is disappointed. She had hoped, I think, that her brother, the Captain, would leave her some money. But those letters are interesting, are they not?'

'The usual poisonous trash.'

'Oh, yes. But interesting. They succeeded in their object too. Mrs Falcon wished me to go down to Meresham and make a scandal with questions. I have been and I have asked some questions. There will also, I think, be a scandal.'

'But you surely don't take this stuff seriously?'

'I do.' Dr Czissar leaned forward. 'And I wish you to do so also, Assistant-Commissioner.'

'But why? The suggestion is, I suppose, that Stenson killed Pewsey. From the facts you have given me, that's obviously absurd. Pewsey was a heavy drinker with a weak heart. He got drunk, had a heart attack and died. The cause of death is confirmed by an autopsy. Perfectly straightforward. If your Mrs Falcon isn't careful, she'll find these accusations of hers landing her in the dock.'

The sad brown eyes blinked. 'But, Assistant-Commissioner, Mrs Falcon makes no accusations. Nor do I think that she believes that there is anything seriously wrong. She wishes only, as I have said, to make a scandal, to revenge herself on her sister-in-law. She comes to me principally for sympathy and because she wishes to talk about the affair. She is very satisfied that I have been to Meresham, but when I returned she even forgot to ask me about the possibility of her brother's death being unnatural. The suggestion in these letters was purely malicious. She had no idea that it was a sound suggestion. No, Assistant-Commissioner, it is not Mrs Falcon but I who make the accusation.'

Mercer sat back. 'And who are you accusing, Doctor?'

Dr Czissar cleared his throat and swallowed hard. 'Attention, please!' he said sharply.

'I am all attention,' snapped Mercer.

'Good. Then I will begin by giving you the facts. The first is contained in Mrs Falcon's letters to herself. Three months after the Captain's death, Mrs Pewsey marries Mr Stenson. "So soon! Strange, is it not?" says Mrs Falcon. It is indeed strange, Assistant-Commissioner. Three months is a very short time in which to bury one husband, adjust one's mind to the idea of widowhood, adjust one's mind again to the idea of replacing the dead husband with a new one, and then marry him. One might reach a decision in so short a time, but actually to marry as well . . . It is, I think, unreal. It seems to me as if the idea of the marriage had been in the mind of Mrs Pewsey and Mr Stenson *before* the Captain died.'

'You can't prove that, Doctor,' said Mercer quickly.

'There is corroborative evidence, Assistant-Commissioner. In the first place, there is the matter of their secrecy. It is not easy, I should think, to keep a secret in a small town like Meresham. Yet, had a member of the Meresham Golf Club not encountered Mr Stenson and the lady in a London hotel the day after they were married, no one in Meresham would even have known that the two had even spoken to one another. Yet, if all was well, they had no reason for secrecy. As the Captain's friend, Mr Stenson would have had a perfectly good reason for seeing Mrs Pewsey in Meresham. But, and I have the authority of Mrs Pewsey's maid for the statement, Stenson had only once been in the Pewseys' house. He had had dinner there one evening a year or more before the Captain died. Secrecy becomes a habit, Assistant-Commissioner. There was secrecy after the Captain's death because there had been need for secrecy before it.

'Another point. There was, I discovered, a great difference between the characters of Mr Stenson and the Captain. Mr Stenson was very popular. He had money. He played golf well. He was noted for his sense of humour. He was handsome. The Captain, however, was most unpopular. He was always trying to do business with people. He drank too much. He played golf badly. He was a bore. Nobody in Meresham could understand why Mr Stenson put up with him. That he did so is most significant.'

Mercer pursed his lips. 'If you don't mind my saying so,

Doctor, I think you've let yourself read more into this business than is really there.'

The cow-like eyes grew rounder and sadder. 'Yes? I will continue. I have interviewed Mrs Pewsey's maid. The house is shut up at the moment, but she was there on the night that the Captain died. Her evidence is interesting – vitally interesting, I think. She heard the Captain return home to die.

'She says that she had never known him so drunk before. He fell up the stairs and stumbled along the passage to his bedroom. And he was talking to himself. He had never done that before. As he passed the door to her room, she heard one sentence clearly. He was mumbling and then he said: "Socrates! What's he mean, Socrates? My name's not Socrates." She heard no more. But she heard enough, I think.'

Mercer threw up his hands. 'I'm sorry, Doctor. I just don't understand. The man was very drunk. Not an unnatural thing in a heavy drinker. Remember, too, that he had been drinking less since he had seen the doctor a week before. He had broken out again. It overstrained his heart. He died. The doctor's autopsy proves it beyond doubt.'

'You think that?' Dr Czissar looked mournful. 'The cause of death was a respiratory failure.'

'Precisely. Loss of breath. Most of us die from it sooner or later.' Mercer stood up. The spell was broken. Dr Czissar was, after all, merely a crank. By freakish chance he had managed to succeed in one or two cases in which the Yard had looked like failing. Now, he had shown himself up. Mercer smiled tolerantly.

'Doctor,' he said, 'you asked me for my advice in this business. I will give it to you. Go back to your landlady and tell her not to be stupid. And forget about the matter yourself. That is all, I think.' He held out his hand.

But Dr Czissar did not rise to take it.

'This, as I have said, is a case of murder, Assistant-Commissioner,' he said deliberately. 'Justice must be done. I have given you the facts. I ask you only to draw conclusions.'

'I have told you my conclusion, Doctor. I repeat it. I think you are making something of nothing.'

Dr Czissar straightened up. 'I have given you the facts without prejudice,' he said. 'Murder has been done. It is clear.'

'Not to me, Doctor.'

'Very well. I will explain.' He cleared his throat, swallowed, and said sharply: 'Attention, please!'

Mercer relapsed into his chair. 'I can spare you two more minutes, Doctor,' he said angrily.

'It will be enough,' said Dr Czissar.

'In the first place, we have the marriage of Mrs Pewsey and Mr Stenson. It is the second mistake they have made. It is a fact that asks questions. There is no doubt that they had been having an affair together for very many months. I think that they must have made up their minds to murder the Captain very early on. Mrs Falcon says that her brother wrote to her nearly a year ago saying that his wife had asked for a divorce and that he had refused. I think we shall find that it was very soon after that that Mr Stenson bought a life insurance policy from the Captain and became so strangely friendly with him. If we wish for more evidence of the affair, I think that we shall find it at the Hotel Metropolis. It was there that the two were seen after their marriage. Doubtless they had been there many times before. So stupid of them to get married so soon after the murder.

'But you are impatient. We come to the murder. The first thing that is curious is this heart trouble of the Captain's. It was not serious enough to kill. The doctor did not think so. He insisted upon an autopsy. But' – Dr Czissar raised a cautionary finger – 'he performed the autopsy himself without consulting the coroner. As I understand English law, he was within his rights if he had the permission of Mrs Pewsey; but what is the value of his autopsy? Great experience is necessary in cases when the cause of death is not reasonably obvious.'

Mercer grunted.

'Next,' pursued Dr Czissar, 'let us consider the manner of the Captain's death. According to the maid, he behaved in an unusual manner. He stumbled and staggered. Now, Assistant-Commissioner, I, too, find that unusual. The Captain was a habitual heavy drinker. In my experience, I have found that such men do *not* usually stumble and stagger from the effects of drink. The Captain was stumbling and staggering. The cause of death was respiratory failure. What is the link between those two facts? I will tell you. It is the word "Socrates".'

'What?'

'You have heard of Socrates, Assistant-Commissioner? Ah, yes. Then you may remember the description of his death. For a time he walks about, then his steps become difficult. Paralysis begins to creep up his legs. He is forced to lie down. The paralysis creeps higher to his chest. And then he dies – of a respiratory failure – paralysis of the lungs. There is only one poison which has that effect. It is the poison which was given to Socrates.'

'You mean hemlock! But . . .'

'Hemlock is the name of the plant from which it is obtained, Assistant-Commissioner. The actual poison is coniine. If the coniine is pure and concentrated, a few drops kill very quickly. An ordinary infusion of hemlock leaves would kill, unless treatment were given, in from two to three hours. There are, I find, quantities of hemlock growing in Mr Stenson's garden. There is no doubt, I think, that when the Captain went into Mr Stenson's house that night, he was given with his whisky an infusion of hemlock leaves. He had been drinking all the evening. He would not notice the taste. But Mr Stenson made the first mistake. He has a sense of humour. He was nervous and worried. He was not used to murder. He turned to his sense of humour for comfort. He tried to make a joke of the situation. He called the Captain "Socrates".'

'But, good heavens, man!' exploded Mercer, 'even if this story is true, how on earth are we going to prove it?'

Dr Czissar got to his feet with dignity. 'I am sure that you will find a way. Coniine remains detectable in the body for many months. An exhumation and an autopsy by an experienced pathologist with no preconceived ideas about cardiac weakness should help you. You will not, I think, be able to prove administration, but I have no doubt that you will be able to build up a circumstantial case strong enough to convict.'

'But what about the woman?' demanded Mercer. 'You said that "they" did the murder.'

'Oh, yes. Mrs Pewsey was certainly an accessory before the fact. There is no doubt in my mind that it was she who prepared the way for the death certificate by sending her husband to the doctor a week before his death. It is not difficult to upset a drinker's heart. Aspirin tablets are almost tasteless dissolved in soda-water. But you may have difficulty in proving anything against her.

'It is Mr Stenson for whom I am sorry,' he went on. 'I have heard so much about the English sense of humour. Now I understand it. I did not think that it would be so macabre, but I like it. It is piquant. Socrates!' He emitted an apologetic little giggle. 'It is really very funny.'

The Case of the Gentleman Poet

IT was after the murderer of Felton Spenser had been tried and convicted that Assistant-Commissioner Mercer finally became resigned to the occasional intrusions of Dr Jan Czissar into the affairs of his department at New Scotland Yard. For that reason alone, the case would be worth reporting. The conversion of an Assistant-Commissioner of New Scotland Yard into an ordinary human being must be reckoned a major triumph of the power of reason over the force of habit. But the case has another claim to the interest of students of criminology in general and, in particular, of those who contemplate committing murders of their own. It demonstrated clearly that the first requisite for the committal of a perfect murder is the omniscience of a god.

The world first heard of the death of Felton Spenser late one January evening, and through the medium of one of the BBC's news bulletins. 'We regret,' said the announcer, in funereal tones, 'to announce the death in London tonight of Mr Felton Spenser, the poet. He was fifty-three. Although Mr Spenser was born in Manchester, the early years of his life were spent in the county of Flint, and it was in praise of the Flint countryside and scenery that much of his poetry was written. His first collection of poems, "The Merciful Light", was published in nineteen-hundred and nine. Mr Marshall Grieve, the critic and a friend of Spenser's, said of him to-night: "He was a gentleman in the Edwardian sense of the word. He was a man without enemies. His verse had a placid limpidity rarely met with nowadays, and it flowed with the lyrical ease of his beloved Dee."'

That was all. It was left to the morning newspapers to disclose the fact that Felton Spenser had been found by his friend, Mr Marshall Grieve, 'the author-critic', shot in his Bloomsbury flat, that there had been a revolver by his side, and that he had recently been suffering from fits of depression. To Assistant-Commissioner Mercer, Detective-Inspector Denton ultimately brought further details.

Felton Spenser had lived in the top flat of a converted house. There were three other flats below his. That on the ground floor was occupied by a dressmaker and her husband, named Lobb. On the first floor lived Mr Marshall Grieve. The second floor was unoccupied. The dead man's flat consisted of two large rooms, used as bedroom and sitting-room respectively, a smaller room used as a study, a kitchen, and a bathroom. It had been in the sitting-room that his body had been found.

At about six thirty that evening, the sound of a shot had come from the top of the house. The dressmaker's husband, Mr Lobb, who had just returned home from his work, ran to the door of his flat. At the same moment, Mr Grieve, who had also heard the shot, had appeared at his door at the head of the first flight of stairs. They had gone up together.

After breaking down the door of Felton Spenser's flat, which had a patent lock on it, they had found Spenser half-sitting, half-lying on the sofa, his arms extended, and his hands turned back as though he had, in the throes of death, gripped the edge of the sofa. The body had been rendered rigid by a cadaveric spasm. The appearance of the wound suggested that when the shot had been fired, the revolver had been within an inch or two of the head.

Grieve stated that Spenser had been suffering for some time from fits of intense depression. He knew of several possible causes of these fits. Spenser had been profoundly disappointed by the reception accorded to a book of his poems published the year before. He had also been in financial difficulties. He had never earned a living from his work, and had lived on a small private income left to him by his wife. He had, however, Grieve believed, been speculating with his capital. He had also lent large sums of money to friends. Grieve had seen him earlier in the day of his death. Spenser had then told him that his affairs were in a bad way, and that he was seeing his solicitor the following day in an effort to salvage some of his losses. This statement was confirmed by the solicitor in question. Shortly before five o'clock in the afternoon of the day on which Spenser had died, he had received a telephone call from Spenser, who asked for an appointment for the following day.

The revolver, reported Denton, was an old pin-fire weapon of French manufacture, and unregistered. Spenser could have come by it in a variety of ways. The same applied to the ammunition. Only one shot had been fired from the revolver. The markings on the bullet extracted from the dead man's head showed that it had come from that particular revolver. The only distinguishing feature about the weapon was a series of marks near the muzzle which suggested that at some time a silencer had been fitted to it. There had been no silencer found in the flat. According to the medical report, the wound showed every sign of having been self-inflicted.

There was, in Denton's opinion, only one curious thing about the case. That thing was the draft of an unfinished letter lying on the desk in the study. It was written in pencil, and much corrected, as if the writer had been choosing his words very carefully. It began:

'As I told you yesterday, I was serious when I said that unless the money was repaid to me by today I would place the matter in the hands of my legal advisers. You have seen fit to ignore my offer. Accordingly, I have approached my solicitor. Need I say that, if I could afford to overlook the whole unpleasant matter, I would do so eagerly? In asking for the return of the money, I . . . .' There the letter stopped.

Mercer considered it. 'Looks pretty straightforward to me,' he said at last. 'According to Grieve, he'd been in the habit of lending people money. It looks as though, having found himself hard pressed, he was trying to get a little of it back. What does his banking account show?'

Denton referred to his notes. 'Well, Sir, he'd certainly got rid of some money. He'd bought one or two parcels of doubtful shares, and lost a bit that way. Six months ago he drew out five hundred in cash. Maybe that was this loan he was trying to get back. Funny idea, though, paying it out in cash. I couldn't find any note of who had it, either. By the look of his place, I should say he was the sort who lights his pipe with important papers. But I thought that letter was a bit curious, Sir. Why should he get up in the middle of writing a letter and shoot himself?'

Mercer pursed his lips. 'Ever heard of impulse, Denton? That's how half the suicides happen. "Suicide while the balance of his mind was disturbed," is the formula. Any life insurance?'

'Not that we can trace, Sir. There's a cousin in Flint who inherits. Executors are Grieve and the solicitor.'

'Grieve's important. What sort of witness will he make?'

'Good, Sir. He looks and talks like an archbishop.'

'All right, Denton. I'll leave it to you.'

And to Denton it was left – for the moment. It was not until the day before the inquest was due to be held that Dr Czissar sent his card into Mercer's office.

For once, Mercer's excuse that he was too busy to see Dr Czissar was genuine. He was due at a conference with the Commissioner and it was to Denton that he handed over the job of dealing with the refugee Czech detective.

Again and again during the subsequent conference he wished that he had asked the Doctor to wait, and interviewed him himself. Since the first occasion on which Dr Czissar had entered New Scotland Yard armed with a letter of introduction from an influential Home Office politician, he had visited Mercer four times. And on every occasion he had brought disaster with him: disaster in the shape of irrefutable proof that he, Dr Czissar, could be right about a case when Assistant-Commissioner Mercer was hopelessly wrong.

When at last he returned to his office, Denton was waiting for him, and the expression of exasperated resignation on Denton's face told him all he wanted to know about Dr Czissar's visit. The worst had happened again. The only thing he could do now was to put as stony a face as possible on the impending humiliation. He set his teeth.

'Ah, Denton!' He bustled over to his desk. 'Have you got rid of Dr Czissar?'

Denton squared his shoulders. 'No, Sir,' he said woodenly. 'He's waiting downstairs to see you.'

'But I told you to see him.'

'I have seen him, Sir. But when I heard what he had to say I thought I'd better keep him here until you were free. It is about this Spenser business, Sir. I'm afraid I've tripped up badly. It's murder.'

Mercer sat down carefully. 'You mean, I suppose, that it's Dr Czissar's *opinion* it was murder?'

'No question of opinion, I'm afraid, Sir. A clear case. He got hold of some of the evidence from that journalist friend of his who lends him his Press pass. I've given him the rest. He saw through the whole thing at once. If I'd have had any gumption I'd have seen through it too. He's darn clever.'

Mercer choked down the words that rose to his lips. 'All right,' he said; 'you'd better bring Dr Czissar up.'

Dr Czissar entered the room exactly as he had entered it many times before – thousands of times, it seemed to Mercer. Inside the door, he clicked his heels, clapped his umbrella to his side as if it were a rifle, bowed, and announced loudly: 'Dr Jan Czissar. Late Prague police. At your service!'

To Mercer it was as familiar as the strains of a detested melody. He said formally: 'How do you do, Doctor? I hear that you have something to tell us about the Spenser case.'

Dr Czissar's pale face relaxed. His tall, plump body drooped into its accustomed position beneath the long, drab raincoat. His brown, cow-like eyes beamed through the thick pebble spectacles. 'You are busy,' he said apologetically. 'It is a small matter.'

'I understand you think that Mr Felton Spenser was murdered.'

The cow-like eyes enlarged. 'Oh, yes. That is what I think, Assistant-Commissioner Mercer. I was a little uncertain as to whether I should come to you about it. The facts on which I base the conclusion I learned from a journalist who tells me things that will interest me for the book I am writing. It is a work of medical jurisprudence. But until Inspector Denton told me that my information was accurate, I was doubtful. You see, it is most important to be accurate in these matters. I was told that the body had been found in a state of cadaveric spasm, and that the revolver was on the floor beside the sofa. The spasm was described to me. I was also told that the finger-prints on the revolver were smeared and indefinite. From the information at my disposal, I had no doubt that Mr Spenser was murdered.'

'And may I ask why, Doctor?'

Dr Czissar cleared his throat and swallowed hard. 'Cadaveric spasm,' he declaimed, as if he were addressing a group of

87

students, 'is a sudden tightening of the muscles of the body at the moment of death, which produces a rigidity which remains until it is succeeded by the lesser rigidity of *rigor mortis*. The limbs of the dead person will thus remain in the positions in which they were immediately before death for some time. Cadaveric spasm occurs most frequently when the cause of death is accompanied by some violent disturbance of the nervous system. In many cases of suicide by shooting through the head, the weapon is held so tightly by the cadaveric spasm in the dead hand that great force is required to remove it.'

Mercer gave a twisted smile. 'And although there was a cadaveric spasm, the revolver was found on the floor. Is that your point? I'm afraid, Doctor, that we can't accept that as proof of murder. A cadaveric spasm may relax after quite a short time. The fact that the hand had not actually retained the weapon is not proof that it did not fire it. So –'

'Precisely,' interrupted Dr Czissar. 'But that was *not* my point, Assistant-Commissioner. According to the medical report, about which the Inspector has been good enough to tell me, the body was in a state of unrelaxed cadaveric spasm when it was examined an hour after it was discovered. The fingers of both hands were slightly crooked, and both hands were drawn backwards almost at right angles to the forearms. But let us think' – he drove one lank finger into his right temple – 'let us think about the effect of a cadaveric spasm. It locks the muscles in the position assumed immediately before death. Very well, then. Mr Spenser's right hand immediately before his death was drawn backwards almost at right-angles to the forearm. Also, the fingers of that hand were slightly crooked. It is not possible, Assistant-Commissioner Mercer, to hold a revolver to the head and pull the trigger with the hand in that position.'

Mercer looked sharply at Denton. 'You saw the body before it was moved. Do you agree with this?'

'I'm afraid I do, Sir,' said Denton dejectedly. 'I ought to have spotted it for myself, but I'm afraid I don't know much about how spasms work.'

'It is not expected that you should, Inspector,' said Dr Czissar kindly. 'These things must be learned. But there is, I think, another conclusion to be drawn from the position of the hands. There is no doubt that Mr Spenser was in the act of rising from the sofa when he was shot. His hands bent in that way could only have been used to raise himself so that he could stand up. The peculiar position of the body thus becomes quite clear.'

'Everything, in fact, becomes quite clear,' snarled Mercer, 'except the identity of the murderer.'

The cow-like eyes gleamed. 'That also is clear, Assistant-Commissioner. As soon as Inspector Denton informed me of the evidence available, I was able to see what had happened.'

Mercer contained himself with an effort. 'And what *did* happen?'

A thin smile stretched the doctor's full lips. He straightened his back, cleared his throat, swallowed hard, and said sharply, 'Attention, please!'

Of all Dr Czissar's mannerisms, it was the one that irritated Mercer most. He sat back in his chair. 'Well, Doctor?'

'In the first place,' said Dr Czissar, 'we have to consider the fact that, on the evidence of the dressmaker, no one left the house after Mr Spenser was killed. Therefore, when the police arrived the murderer was still there. Inspector Denton tells me also that the entire house, including the empty flat on the second floor, was searched by the police. Therefore, the murderer was one of the three persons in the house at the time – the dressmaker, Mrs Lobb, her husband, who returned home before the shot was heard, and Mr Grieve. But which?

'Mr Lobb states that, on hearing the shot, he ran to the door of his flat and looked up the stairs, where he saw Mr Grieve appear at the door of his flat. They then went up together to the scene of the crime. If both these men are innocent and telling the truth, then there is an absurdity: for if neither of them shot Mr Spenser, then Mrs Lobb shot him, although she was downstairs at the time of the shot. It is not possible. Nor is it possible for either of the men to have shot him, unless they are both lying. Another absurdity. We are faced with the conclusion that someone has been ingenious.

'How was the murder committed?' Dr Czissar's cow-like eyes sought piteously for understanding. 'How? There is only one clue in our possession. It is that a microscopic examination of the revolver-barrel showed Inspector Denton that at some time a silencer had been fitted to it. Yet no silencer is found in Mr

Spenser's flat. We should not expect to find it, for the revolver probably belongs to the murderer. Perhaps the murderer has the silencer? I think so. For only then can we explain the fact that when a shot is heard, none of the suspects is in Mr Spenser's room.'

'But,' snapped Mercer, 'if a silencer had been fitted, the shot would not have been heard. It *was* heard.'

Dr Czissar smiled. 'Therefore, we must conclude that two shots were fired, one to kill, the other to be heard.'

'But only one shot had been fired from the revolver that killed Spenser.'

'Oh, yes, Assistant-Commissioner, that is true. But the murder was, I believe, committed with two revolvers. I believe that Mr Grieve went to Mr Spenser's flat, armed with the revolver you found, at about six o'clock, or perhaps earlier. There was a silencer fitted to the revolver, and when the opportunity came, he shot Mr Spenser through the head. He them removed the silencer, smudged the finger-prints on the revolver and left it by Mr Spenser on the floor. He then returned to his own flat and hid the silencer. The next thing he did was to wait until Mr Lobb returned home, take a second revolver, go up into the empty flat, and fire a second, but blank, shot.

'Mr Lobb – he will be the most valuable witness for the prosecution – says in his evidence that, on hearing the shot, he ran to his door and saw Mr Grieve coming out of his flat. It sounds very quick of him, but I think it must have taken Mr Lobb longer than he thinks. He would, perhaps, look at his wife, ask her what the noise was, and *then* go to his door. Yet even a few seconds would be time for Mr Grieve to fire the shot, descend one short flight of stairs, and pretend to be coming out of his door.'

'I gathered that you had Grieve in mind,' said Mercer, 'but may I remind you that this is all supposition? Where is the proof? What was Grieve's motive?'

'The proof,' said Dr Czissar comfortably, 'you will find in Mr Grieve's flat – the silencer, the second revolver, and perhaps pin-fire ammunition. He will not have got rid of these things for fear of being seen doing so. Also, I suggest that Mr Lobb, the dressmaker's husband, be asked to sit in his room and listen to two shots: one fired in Mr Spenser's room from the revolver that killed Mr Spenser, the other, a blank shot, fired in the empty flat. You will find, I think, that he will swear that it was the second shot he heard. The two noises will be quite different.

'For the motive, I suggest that you consider Mr Grieve's financial arrangements. Some months ago, Mr Spenser drew five hundred pounds in cash from his bank. There is no doubt, I think, that Mr Grieve had it. While we were waiting for you, Assistant-Commissioner, I suggested to the Inspector that some information about Mr Grieve's income would be helpful. Mr Grieve, we find, earns a little money writing for a weekly journal. He is also an undischarged bankrupt. He would therefore prefer to receive so large a sum in notes instead of by cheque. Also, we have only his word that Mr Spenser lent money freely. I have no doubt that Mr Grieve obtained the money to invest on Mr Spenser's behalf, and that he took it for himself. Perhaps you will find some of it in his flat. Mr Spenser had discovered the theft, and threatened to expose him. The letter he was writing was to Mr Grieve. But Mr Grieve did not wait to receive it. He decided to kill Mr Spenser. The fact that he had this old revolver and silencer no doubt suggested the method. But, like all other clever criminals, he is stupid. He makes a statement about his dead friend. "A man without enemies," he says. So strange to comment on the fact, one thinks. So few of us have enemies. But when we see that Mr Grieve wishes it to be thought that his friend suicided himself, we understand.'

Dr Czissar sighed and stood up. 'So kind of you to receive me, Assistant-Commissioner Mercer. Good afternoon.'

'One moment, Doctor.'

Mercer had risen to his feet. There was nothing left for him to say that would change the fact of his defeat, and he knew it. The hope that Dr Czissar would one day prove that he was no more infallible than other men had been deferred too often for him to derive any comfort from it. He did the only thing he could do under the circumstances.

'We're very much obliged to you, Doctor,' he said. 'We'll always be glad of any help you can give us.'

Dr Czissar's pale face reddened. 'You are too kind,' he

stammered. And then, for once, his English deserted him. 'It is to me a great . . .' he began, and then stopped. 'It is for me . . .' he said again. He could get no further, and abandoned the attempt to do so. Crimson in the face, he clicked his heels at each of them in turn. 'An honour,' he said.

Then he was gone. 'He's left his umbrella behind,' said Denton. 'Maybe he'll come back for it.'

Middle

IT was twenty-five years before I wrote another short story. Five years of the interval were spent in the army. I had an eventful war, and for a time after it took to film-making as a writer-producer. As a producer I was a flop but as a writer I had a series of successes. A screenplay I had written for an Ealing film was nominated for an Oscar. For the American Academy to nominate a British writer for his work on a British film was at that time unusual. I was flattered and should have been encouraged as well, but by the mid-fifties I was beginning to have doubts about film-making as even a part-time occupation for a writer who enjoyed his work most when he was writing to be read. I had begun writing novels again and, although I now had friends in the film industry with whom I enjoyed working, I had no sense of commitment to the over-indulged accountant and his lay-preaching master who tried to lead it.

The children had grown up and gone back to America. Louise was working again, and well, as a fashion illustrator. I could pay off the back income tax by selling the house in Pelham Crescent and we could start again; but we didn't. The Suez Canal was about to be re-opened. We went to Marseille and boarded a Messageries Maritimes boat bound for South-East Asia. We returned on a Rotterdamsche-Lloyd liner crammed with Dutch colonial refugees from Java. In the Red Sea the ship lost a propeller blade and we had to jolt home at reduced speed.

It was not a happy return. A few months later Louise divorced me. The divorce was 'amicable'; that is to say we both remained mindful of good times past as well as of changed minds. We had been married eighteen years.

With the Pelham Crescent house sold and the proceeds from a sale of movie rights in a novel, there was enough both to pay

off the back income tax and to set Louise up in a New York
studio apartment. She took the bits of furniture she liked; I put
my books and writing table into storage and rented a furnished
flat. There, I wrote the script of a film that turned out to be the
first of a new wave of disaster movies; I also wrote the first
chapter of a novel to be called *Passage of Arms*. At that point I
was asked if I would like to go and work in Hollywood.

It was not the first time I had been asked. Just after the war,
and before the McCarthy witch hunts began, I had been
assured over expensive hotel lunches that a fortune awaited me
in California. The persuaders, from Leland Hayward to Irving
(Swifty) Lazar, had been charming and sometimes even
entertaining, but I had always resisted the call. I knew that my
reputation as a storyteller and a screenwriter was worth more in
America than it was in England but I liked my country then and
believed in its future. I had helped to elect the Attlee
government, I could call Michael Foot a friend and was
indebted to him for letting me meet Nye Bevan. True, Bevan
had spent half an hour or more trying to persuade me to write a
film based on the mystery of the Junius letters, but it had been a
boozy evening and after all, Dumas had made entertaining
fiction out of old French political scandals.

The French, too, I would remind myself had made superb
films for French-speaking audiences without bankrupting
themselves or corrupting the French theatre from which the
native cinema drew its acting and directing strengths. Its
writers for the screen had often been poets first. In England we
had been told that we had to make films that would penetrate
the American market and earn dollars. It should be easy we
were told; we and our cousins had a common language; we had
been gallant allies and fought the good fight for the soul of
Europe. Ask them in Madison, Ohio, the heart of America! But
all we penetrated in the end were the 'art house' circuits of the
big cities; but probably no more deeply than Italian films with
English subtitles.

The McCarthy inquisitions and the black lists they spawned
had their compensations. Exiled writers and directors made
Europe the centre of excellence for international film production. Hollywood was where the best all-American movies were
still made. The days of the Hollywood major studios and the

vertically integrated monopolies of which they were a part were now numbered. The advent of network television and American anti-trust laws together brought them down. The first of the studios to rise again was Universal and it rose with the help of the talent agency MCA who bought it and made a television programme factory out of it, the first of its kind.

I was only dimly aware of this development. My experience of television was limited to the serialization of a novel of mine by one of the commercial production companies. I attended some of the rehearsals – it was to be transmitted 'live' – and the whole thing was quite unnerving. I was told that filming the rehearsals and afterwards cutting the bits together would be impossibly expensive. I was surprised when Alfred Hitchcock, who was then making at Universal a one-hour anthology series called 'Suspicion', asked me to write an original screenplay for the show. Of course, with an 'anthology' series there were no series characters – the format was that of a short three-act play – and, of course, the great man did not ask me himself. Joan Harrison, the 'Suspicion' producer, did all the commissioning and I was one among those commissioned. I called my piece *The Eye of Truth* and when produced it starred Joseph Cotten and the young George Peppard. It went down well in America and probably served to remind MGM of my existence.

My producer at their Culver City studios was Julian Blaustein, one of the new corps of semi-independent producers created to fight the MGM battle to retain the audiences drifting away from their movie theatres and drive-ins to the increasingly accessible pleasures of colour TV. The dreadful Louis B. Mayer had long gone and the head of the studio was now Sol Siegel, but writers were still allocated offices on the writers' floor of the Irving Thalberg building and still had to seek special permission to do their work at home. The day when William Faulkner, working at home, had been summoned by Thalberg to an urgent script conference and found to be at home, two thousand miles away in Oxford, Mississippi had not been forgotten. Nothing had been forgotten. It was still the custom when an expensive British writer was hired and reported for work for him to be paraded for inspection by the top brass of the front office in the producers' dining-room on the fourth floor. It was the only time he would be invited to eat there and he was expected to speak only when spoken to. The food was dull, no wine was served (producers had bar cupboards in their offices) and the only person of interest to me there, aside from Blaustein my escort, was Arthur Freed who had produced all the great MGM musicals. He, however, was there just to eat and all I got from him was a nod between mouthfuls. It was left to Eddie Mannix, who had been a trouble-shooter for Thalberg and was the senior old timer there, to ask the test questions.

'Where are you going to be staying?'

'I'm renting a house on Camden Drive.'

'That the one on the corner of the seven hundred block, the one Vincent Minelli had?'

'That's the one.'

'Ever hear the story about William Faulkner working at home when he was on our payroll?'

It was one of the oldest Hollywood stories but I must have said that I had heard it too patiently. He gave me a sharp look.

'Writers come and go,' he said; 'anyone ever tell you that when those bigheads over at Western Electric brought in sound they ruined a great industry?'

'I've heard it said.'

'I'll bet you have. And there are still quite a lot of us who think it's true.'

'If you want to know all about the silent days,' said my producer, 'Eddie knows where all the bodies are buried. But right now we ought to be getting back to work.' When we were outside he said: 'You won't have to go through that again.'

Julian Blaustein was a Harvard man and his best-known film at that time was *Broken Arrow* which had starred James Stewart. The film he had hired me to write was based on a Hammond Innes novel called *The Wreck of the Mary Deare*. It starred Gary Cooper as a rogue sea captain used as a fall guy by marine insurance swindlers. The story is about his fight to regain his reputation as an employable ship's captain. It was a well-mounted film in the MGM tradition with a fine supporting cast directed by Michael Anderson; and it was a flop; not commercially perhaps, but I could only see its failings. I think we had the wrong star. The part called for an angrier, hungrier healthier actor than Gary Cooper. Poor old Coop had prostate trouble. Where in the film there should have been fire and fight there was only a weary desperation. You did not blame the woman for her final rejection of him. This was not the Coop of *High Noon* or *Mr Deeds Goes to Town*. He made only one more picture before he died.

At Culver City MGM had taken one more step on the way down. Sol Siegel's new policy was to remake old hits. Even I knew that this was wrong. The received wisdom about remakes was that it was the good properties you made again, not the successful ones. Spectacles like *Ben Hur* and *The Ten Commandments* could be remade because they could always be improved technically. Artistic development was a different matter. *The Maltese Falcon* by Dashiell Hammett was twice made into below average Warner Bros. B-movies before the 1941 version directed by John Huston with Humphrey Bogart and Mary Astor turned out to be a classic of the genre. That sort of success can never be calculated. What Julian Blaustein had now been assigned to produce was a remake of an old silent hit *The Four Horsemen of the Apocalypse*. Julian wanted me to write a new script setting the story in World War Two instead of World War One. He ran the old film for me in the Thalberg building projection room.

I had first seen it at the age of twelve while on holiday in Broadstairs. It was Rudolf Valentino's introduction to a world audience and I remembered some of his scenes, but what I remembered best were the war sequences. The character of the tango-dancing playboy played by Valentino seemed to me to have no possible counterpart in the second war context; and if the heroes and France were so different, so were the enemy villains. A reformed playboy in the Resistance? Sure, why not? But I did not want to write it. I was tired of World War Two heroics, even the genuine kind. Julian was disappointed with me and did not ask me to work for him again.

I went back to writing *Passage of Arms* and passed the test for a regular Californian driving licence. I made friends. Later that year Joan Harrison and I were married.

Joan was an Oxford graduate (St Hugh's, Modern Greats) and had come to Hollywood with the Hitchcock family (Hitch, Alma and their daughter Pat) in 1938 to work for Selznick on *Rebecca*. She had been the writer on other Hitchcock pictures, notably *Foreign Correspondent*, but left for RKO to be a producer on her own account. She made several successful pictures there, starring Robert Montgomery, before Howard Hughes bought the studio and delivered an ultimatum. It was addressed to all contract producers but it was meant for Joan Harrison. In future, he said, all RKO pictures would be about one of only two things, fighting and fornication. He did not like women in positions of authority. She had taken the hint and moved to New York as a 'live' television producer. When MCA moved into Universal Hitch invited her back to take charge of his television productions. She had the authority of an executive producer which in Hollywood is considerable; for many years she ran Hitchcock television. She hired writers, directors and actors to do work that displayed their talents to advantage. Some valuable professional careers had their beginnings in the Hitchcock shows. In Hollywood Joan was an important person.

This importance had its drawbacks and I soon discovered some of them. In the small cities and suburbs of West Los Angeles those who dealt with the public in an official capacity, the counter clerks behind the grilles in local and state government offices, were always very polite and helpful and were obviously trained to be so; elected officials like to protect their majorities. However their friendliness was not wholly innocent. When the clerk looked at the name on the form and asked "Are you the writer?" no literary interest could be assumed; what the clerk was probably wondering was whether or not your presence before him or her was worth a call to Hedda Hopper's office or, maybe, Louella Parsons'. Applications for wedding licences could be newsworthy, of course, but the preliminaries to the licence could be important leads. In the state of California at that time both applicants for a licence had to have Wasserman tests to prove that they did not have syphilis, and the tests had to be done by state-licensed pathologists. Obviously, the two of you did not go to the same clinic. The business of getting the actual licence with both your names on it was much simpler because the applicants did not have to appear in person – they could be legally represented – and because the licence was issued not by the City of Los Angeles but by the County, all four hundred square miles of it. A Universal Studios attorney who liked Joan and approved of my books sent two of his legal staff out to a desert town near

Bakersfield where there was a County official whose discretion, for some mysterious reason, could be absolutely relied upon. The legal assistants, armed with sworn copies of my English divorce papers and our Wasserman test results, had no difficulty at all. The wedding itself would take place in San Francisco. Hitch, who would give the bride away, made the arrangements. His attorney there had clout enough to persuade a Superior Court judge to forgo his Saturday golf game and open up his chambers in the City Hall. It had to be a Saturday because a short weekend was the only time that could be spared away from the studios. The attorney reserved a suite in my name at the Mark Hopkins Hotel. The security was very tight.

It was I who blew it. The 'maid' – that is, the woman who came in daily at Camden Drive to tidy and make the bed – also did the routine marketing that kept the refrigerator stocked. She was a quiet ladylike woman of fifty or so and she drove an old Buick that looked better in the driveway than my rented Chevrolet. I knew that she was registered with Central Casting and that she did walk-ons and extra work, but many of the Beverly Hills maids did that. What I had not realized was that, whatever their part-time activities, they all acted as informers for the syndicated gossip columnists; they were paid by results, but they were well paid; they were pros.

All I did on the Friday morning was change the usual weekend shopping list a bit and ask her to buy some smoked salmon at the good delicatessen on Beverly Drive. She asked whether I wanted the champagne and smoked salmon for Saturday or Sunday? Sunday, I told her, when I got back from San Francisco. Santa Glen market was the best for champagne; did I want the best? Indeed I did. That was all. Within an hour Joan had Louella Parsons calling her at the studio. Louella wanted the exclusive story on the wedding. If she had the exclusive she would see that we had an easy ride; if not, presumably, she would see that we had a rough one. Joan agreed at once to the exclusivity; she had always believed that Louella was less bitchy than Hedda Hopper.

I found Louella's easy ride fairly bumpy. Hitch, who with Alma was to be a witness of the wedding, had organized it with an eye to its potential entertainment value as shrewd as if we had been Cary Grant and Ingrid Bergman. What Joan and I had not realized was that the City Hall in San Francisco, the place of our wedding, was normally closed for business on Saturdays and that its handsome steps and massive portico became the weekend rendezvous for all the red-eye winos, hop-heads, drunks and deadbeats in the city. Red-eye was a syrupy Californian muscatel heavily fortified with cheap grain alcohol and it had a distinctive smell. The judge, already sullen because of his lost golf, was in a bad temper by the time he reached us. He cheered up, though, when he recognized Hitch and saw all the photographers. By the time he had married us he had mellowed considerably and even offered to run through the ceremony again for the benefit of those photographers who still had film left. It was I who rejected this offer and I was supported by Hitch who had brought his own Leica and planned shots of the happy couple standing among the supine drunks on the steps outside. By the time we reached our suite at the Mark Hopkins and the friends who had flown up from Los Angeles to help us celebrate, we needed strong drink. So did the judge and one or two photographers. The judge became tipsy and telephoned his wife to invite her to join the party. Mercifully she didn't; but he was the last to leave. It had been a long day.

At three o'clock in the morning the telephone woke me. It was the *Daily Express* in London calling. The Louella Parsons report had reached them; was it true that I had married again? I complained that it was three o'clock on Sunday morning. They said that it was early Sunday evening there and that Express newspapers had always been very nice to me. About Joan Harrison, hadn't she been married to Clark Gable? No, I was her first husband. Yes, she had sometimes partnered Charlie Chaplin at tennis; she was a good doubles player and he liked to win.

A few days later the newspaper cuttings arrived from England. The *Daily Express* had a big picture of Joan in Clark Gable's arms: she in a ball gown, he in white tie and tails. Before it was televised the annual Academy Awards dinner used to be a dressier and altogether more attractive affair. The picture of Joan was a good one, and she was not displeased by its reappearance.

When the lease on the Camden Drive house ran out we brought a small house in Bel Air. Joan had some furniture in store from a house she had owned in the Holmby Hills. I sent to England for my books and writing table.

Everybody who has ever been to the cinema knows what Los Angeles looks like; they have all seen it in Hollywood films; they've seen the scruffy palm trees and perhaps known enough to realize that they were not date or coconut palms; but they have also seen the Bermuda grass lawns, the oleanders in flower and the bush bougainvillaeas; they've seen the tall fern trees, the orange groves and the freshwater swimming pools. It looks like the picture postcards of some sub-tropical paradise. The postcards lie; some of the plants may be sub-tropical, but this was never a paradise; it was and remains a desert. Until 1939, when the Los Angeles aqueduct, all three hundred miles of it, was completed and water diverted from the Owens river lake and the Colorado river could flow into the LA reservoirs, fresh water came only from a few artesian wells, sunk by the oil companies and the big citrus growers. Modern Los Angeles is a product of its aqueduct, the Owens river water and a distribution system that meters the supply to every building and household in the city. Hosepipes are used instead of brooms to clear leaves and other rubbish away. To water the garden you turn on the sprinkler system. Water gets expensive only when you first fill the swimming pool; the real cost of the pool is in the maintenance of it afterwards.

Our house was at the top of a steep cul-de-sac off Stone Canyon Road a mile past the Bel Air Hotel. It had been built in 1940 when every house in the area was different from its neighbours, domestic architects were landscape designers first and labour was cheap. Before the house was built the canyon wall above it had been completely terraced and secured with properly made paths and fieldstone retaining walls. Then it had been planted with fern trees and massed camellias. There was no swimming pool but the house was in the attractive two-storey Monterey style which had evolved on the littoral north and south of the Monterey peninsula. It suited that area better than the Spanish hacienda and adobe mission variations that had come from Mexico. In a Los Angeles canyon, though, it had its disadvantages.

Weather men in California used to complain that they had no weather to forecast, only a climate on which to report. Weather reporting was, indeed, monotonous; but the climate could play tricks. Winter did not always come when it was due, in the first quarter of the year, when Pacific storm fronts brought a few inches of rain. Sometimes the storms missed by going north or south; occasionally they hit with a combined force and the usual few inches became a drenching tropical storm causing disastrous landslides and flooding which would turn the floors of the canyon into rivers again. On the other hand, winter sometimes did not come at all. The first Christmas we spent in our Bel Air house was like that. In LA November is often the hottest month of the year with day temperatures in the high nineties. In December it usually cools off and Christmas decorations on the Wilshire Boulevard shopping strips are allowed to look less ridiculous. That December, though, day temperatures stayed in the nineties and seemed inclined to stay there. The usual twenty-degree fall as the sun went down and the cold night air slid down the canyon walls did not happen; a parching santana wind from the mountains inland kept the temperature up. On New Year's eve we were going to a party at the Lederers. It was the party to be at and all our friends would be there. Black tie was obligatory. However, I had brought my dinner jacket from England and it had been made with the English climate in mind. I drove us to the party in my shirt sleeves. On the flat land of Beverly Hills, it was slightly cooler, but only slight. At the end of January there were a few sprinkles of rain, nothing much; after that there was no rain for ten months.

The year after that was a busy one for both of us. Joan had been producing two television shows, the one-hour versions of 'Alfred Hitchcock Presents' and 'Suspicion'. I had abandoned the disaster of Marlon Brando's *Mutiny on the Bounty* in time to stay sane and had started a novel called *The Light of Day*. I had also realized that in the canyons of Los Angeles there was always a danger of fire. The year before there had been a brush fire in Laurel Canyon near West Hollywood and Aldous Huxley whose house there was damaged lost some valuable papers. I still wrote by hand and used a copy typist for first drafts. Someone advised me to buy a fireproof safe to keep the manuscript in until it was typed. I did so and felt able to forget about fire risks.

Monday the 6th of November 1961 began as a beautiful day. It was hot but it was dry and the air was so clear that you could see for miles. Just after eight Joan left, as usual, to drive across to the San Fernando Valley and the Universal Studios in what was becoming known as North Hollywood. I went to my workroom on the first floor and began to write. Shortly afterwards a woman arrived to do some copy typing. I had been editing a book of pieces for my London publisher and the finished typescript was in work. She wheeled the typewriter into the shade of the patio. The santana wind was blowing in gusts now and the temperature was already in the nineties and rising.

The santana is a desert wind and seasonal like the mistral and the sirocco, and it resembles them, too, in its effects on human behaviour. People become irritable and emotionally unstable; blood pressure and pulse rates rise; arguments and fights break out more easily. I was not surprised when the typist said she had called a friend in Laurel Canyon who said there was a brush fire over in the valley. The friend, she said, was frightened because she had no car that day and needed company. I told her to go if she wanted to and to take the typescript with her; she could finish the work at home if she liked. She was off immediately.

I went back to work, but almost immediately had to break off again. Nellie, our housekeeper, came upstairs to tell me that the local CBS radio station was reporting a serious brush fire. It had been started somewhere near Sherman Oaks by a spark from a bulldozer blade striking a rock. The fire was eight miles away, but the santana was now blowing at gale force. I asked Nellie if she was worried. She said 'no', but thought that it might be a good idea to turn on the sprinkler system. It wasn't the gardener's day to come to us but she knew how to do it. She would also get the garden hose out, just in case.

I said fine and went back to work. That was just after nine o'clock. At about half past nine Nellie came up again to tell me that the roof of the house was on fire.

The Monterey house was a two-storey building, the ground floor built of brick, often reinforced with steel against earthquake movement, and the upper floor a lath-and-plaster structure with clapboard sidings and a handsome balcony shaded from the sun by a broad pitched roof. The roof tiles, though, were shingles; that is to say they were not of inexpensive red earthenware but of a costly hardwood, usually seasoned oak.

The roof itself was not in fact yet on fire. What had happened was that the santana, now gusting at sixty or more, was carrying with it large pieces of flaming debris. What was on fire on our roof was a large tree branch which had been borne by the wind from the garden of a burning house a quarter of a mile away along the canyon. We were by now in the path of a fire storm.

Neither Nellie Williams nor I yet understood this, however. Nellie, who had been born and raised in Stepney and learned to cook as a below-stairs servant in a big house, had lived through the London blitz and knew how to face danger without fuss; you collected all the valuables you could carry and took them to the nearest shelter. I tried to extinguish the fire on the roof with water from the hose. When I started there was still enough pressure in the system for me to reach the burning branch, but that did not last. Before long the water from the hose had become a useless trickle. A neighbour lower down the hill had a flat asphalt roof to stand on but with no water he was having to use a broom to sweep the burning bits off. Our pitched roof was burning in several places by then. It was time to go.

The only bits of our place that did not burn were the garages. They were on a forecourt thirty feet or so below the house and below the fiery air stream that was taking the fire towards the Pacific coast. It was moving across the wild brush on the hill above us, the radio said, at the rate of thirteen acres a minute. One acre of dry sumac brush is as combustible as four hundred gallons of spilled petrol and the updraught it created turned the singing noise of the santana wind into a howl. But it howled over our garages. Nellie and I sat there between our cars watching the house burn. We were both suffering quite unpleasantly from smoke inhalation. Among the things brought out by Nellie was half a bottle of vodka. She wasn't a drinker but on that occasion she made an exception; and it was she who reminded me that I had things to do.

'I've got Mrs Ambler's fur coat and jewellery,' she said, 'and there was one of her nighties in the washing machine, but you'd better start thinking about a hotel. If you're waiting for the fire department to come and put it out, forget it. If they were coming they'd have been here an hour ago. Besides, what could they do? They've got no water. Don't worry about me. I'll move in with Rose.'

Rose was her sister, a skilled lady's maid and dinner party waitress, who had an apartment and who would certainly iron the rescued nightie before Joan had need of it. I walked down the hill to the man with the flat roof and asked if his phone was still working. He told me to help myself, but that it did no good calling the fire department. I had no address book but knew the Universal Studio number too well to need one by then. Joan knew, of course, all about the fire but not that we were among the victims. I asked her to get us into the Bel Air Hotel because that was the nearest. She called back five minutes later to say that the Bel Air had evacuated their staff but that she had secured the last available bungalow at the Beverly Hills Hotel. I said that I would be with her there as soon as possible; almost as an afterthought I asked her to call our business manager and report our situation. She said the number was in our address books. I had to break the news that unless Nellie had thought to save one, we had no address books. None of the people who mattered to us was in the telephone directory.

The man with the flat roof had come down now. He offered me a beer, which I drank gratefully, and a peanut butter sandwich which my smoke-dried saliva glands refused to accept. A voice over the radio warned those of us still in Bel Air not to leave our properties unattended. There were already reports coming in of looters. And the fire was reported to have jumped the Sepulveda freeway and to be in Brentwood. I rejoined Nellie in the garage.

The whole of our house was on fire now and I was in time to see the upper storey collapse into the lower. The heat was appalling. Luckily there was a stand pipe on the garage level which was still delivering a trickle of water clean enough to drink and to cool our faces. The wind and the updraught from the fires were doing strange things now and with a whoosh the whole hillside above us burst into flames. There were no buildings up there at that time; it was wild and brush-covered with a few stunted trees. We had known there was wild life there because we could hear the coyotes at night and deer

107

would damage the chain link fence which was there to keep them out, but mostly the animals had remained unseen. Now, suddenly they were all running for their lives down towards the floor of the canyon. The deer came first; but the rabbits soon followed and there were animals I did not recognize, stoat-like creatures, feral cats and tree rats. Many of those with long hair were on fire as they ran and where they went fresh fires were started. I began to worry about the garage roof. We had a short hose there, the one the gardener used for sweeping leaves off the forecourt, but there was not enough water pressure to deal with any more airborne fire bombs. We could only wait and hope now.

The radio was still bleating about the need to guard against looters. I asked Nellie what she thought.

'It's a lot of nonsense,' she said; 'apart from us, there's only two kinds of people with transport in Bel Air, the gardeners and the pool men. The gardeners are all Mexican or Japanese; the pool maintenance men are mostly white. It's the blacks the police are afraid of. They know that if the blacks really started to move in, they'd have to call in the army to stop them.'

I thought she was exaggerating. This was two years before the first big Los Angeles riots devastated the Watts area. I thought that the covenant in the title deeds of the house which prohibited our selling it to an 'Ethiopian' a quaint survival of a bygone era. I was wrong. That same euphemism for 'black' or 'Negro' was still in use by the Immigration service. It was normal in Bel Air, as normal as the high fire risk and as normal as the rage I learned to feel when I saw a gawping tourist toss a glowing cigarette butt out of a car window into the scrub at the side of the road.

Some time after three in the afternoon we saw our first fireman of the day. He was a middle-aged man with a smoke-blackened face streaked by rivers of sweat. We had reported a fire at eight forty that morning. He was checking up on those who had called in. He did not apologize for our having received no help and I did not raise the subject. I asked how many houses he had on his list. 'Nearly two hundred,' he said; 'but we're still counting.' His voice was like mine, a smokey croak. In some sections it was every house, in others, like ours, the fire had skipped. He was putting us down as a total loss. What about looters? He said he hadn't heard of any looting. There had been some trouble at Zsa Zsa Gabor's house. She was away and the Bel Air Patrol had caught what they thought was a souvenir hunter. He turned out to be a fan of hers, a student from UCLA who was rescuing her silver from the house and throwing it into her swimming pool. Not a bad idea if you had a pool. Best place to be if you had a house on fire. I told him about my fireproof safe and he looked over our bits of salvage. Apart from Joan's fur coat there were three pictures. Two were Venard trompe-l'oeils that belonged to Lesley Blanch who had left them with us for safe keeping; the third was a John Piper canvas which we had bought earlier that year and of which we were already fond.

'I wouldn't worry about looters,' the fireman said, 'but I'd get that fur coat out of here or it'll smell of smoke for ever. And I wouldn't stick around. The police are closing both Bel Air gates. If you get out you won't get in again today. But you won't want to will you? It'll be twenty-four hours at least before it's cool enough to get near that safe.'

Nellie left soon after in her car taking Joan's things and promising to telephone our business manager to report what the fireman had said. I stayed there until it was dark, drinking water from the stand pipe and dozing in my car. I was feeling quite ill by then and it was Dexter, son of another unburnt neighbour, who drove me to the Beverly Hills Hotel.

There I found that everything that could be done had been done. Joan had bought me a toothbrush, shaving things and a change of underwear from the hotel drugstore. Nellie had enlisted the aid of Dudley Walker, an English manservant who had been Barbara Hutton's butler, then her son Lance Reventlow's minder and valet and then, when the young master had killed himself in a sports car race, a freelance valet and party barman. He was a good man in emergencies. I found myself the temporary possessor of a Sulka dressing-gown, silk pyjamas and monogrammed slippers. The monogram wasn't mine but the slippers fitted. I managed to get out of the clothes I was wearing and soap myself under the shower before I passed out.

I came to in bed with a doctor listening to my chest and tapping it. 'Delayed shock,' he said; 'you fainted. No damage, though you're going to have difficulty swallowing for a few days.

109

Smoke. I'm going to give you a shot now and you'll go to sleep for a couple of hours. When you wake you'll be hungry. I'd order something soft like scrambled eggs, hash browns and coffee. When you've eaten you should go back to sleep almost at once and sleep until morning.'

The shot worked as he had said it would. When I woke the first time I found that Dudley had been in and taken all my filthy clothes; they would be returned clean and wearable in the morning. I never found out the name of the shot that worked so well. As the taste of smoke went away I forgot to ask; and I had other things to worry about.

Two days after the fire the count of houses totally destroyed by it had gone up to four hundred and eighty-four. With our business manager I went out to inspect the remains of ours and to take photographs for the insurance and income tax deduction claims. We were under-insured, of course, like everyone else, and in the Californian real estate boom then in progress that meant that our lost house had had a market value of twice what we had paid for it, and four times the value for which it was insured. At some point we would have to decide whether or not to rebuild. All I wanted just then, however, was to go and get at the safe and retrieve my manuscript.

The safe, we found, had fallen from the upper floor right through the ground floor into what had been the crawl space under the steel-grade beams of the foundations. I had left the safe key in the lock – it had been protection against fire, not theft – and in its fall it had snapped off. The safe, however, was intact. Our man of business said that we would have to get the safe-crackers in.

They came two days later and I was there to meet them. They were an impressive team, serious men in immaculate sky-blue coveralls with the worded BONDED in white, back and front, above their firm's name. Their vehicles were impressive too: small armoured vans, one towing a compressor, the other a generator of the kind of energy that turns ferro-concrete to butter in seconds. Both the vans and the towed equipment were spotlessly clean. So were the men. Two of them walked up to the ruins with me and I showed them the fallen safe.

'What's in it?' the head man asked; 'anything heavy?'

'Papers.'

110

They put two canvas slings under the safe and lifted it up on to the patio, door uppermost. The head man examined the broken end of the key then nodded to his colleague who went back to the vans for tools – tools for lock-picking I had hoped – but all he brought back with him was a long chisel and a sledge hammer. The chisel he applied to the hinge side of the safe door. His leader then swung the hammer and gave the chisel a sharp tap. The door of the safe popped open to reveal a mass of grey ash that turned to powder when it was touched. The only recognizable object there was my UK passport. The blue cover had turned to black toffee, but my name was readable.

'It was supposed to be fireproof,' I protested.

'No,' said the safe cracker and pointed to a code number stamped on the maker's tag welded to the door. 'That means fire resistant. This box would stand a thousand-degree heat for half an hour. This has had two thousand degrees or more for over six hours. Look at that steel I-beam down there. It bent, almost melted. Those papers didn't burn – not enough air in there – but they sure cooked.'

I took the passport, to show at the British consulate if they wanted proof of loss. I didn't waste time with the remains of *The Light of Day*. Joan and I had decided to go to England for Christmas and see our families. Before we could do that, however, we had to find somewhere to live. The Beverly Hills Hotel had been helpful but was proving astonishingly expensive. We needed a furnished house and quickly. Other Bel Air and Brentwood refugees were after the same thing. We took the first on offer that had the number of rooms we needed and was available that week. It was on North Roxbury Drive and looked inoffensive enough from the outside. Inside there was a lot of fairly nasty pink. My work room had once been a teenage girl's bedroom and she had had a collection of dolls, dozens of them in glass cases which lined the walls. They had no merit, historical or artistic, that I could discern; they were just toy department dolls that looked as if they had been bought in the fifties. I tried to have them removed but they were itemized on the inventory and, I was told, highly valued by the owner of the house. Nellie, who knew something about antique dolls, said they were rubbish; but she was also entertained by the fact that I would have to put up with them. She had a Yorkshire terrier named Winston whose piercing yap I had objected to more than once. The effects of the smoke inhalation were more or less forgotten but the sense of bereavement with which I was trying to come to terms was of an unfamiliar kind. I found myself behaving absurdly.

People in Hollywood work long hours and there are fewer big parties than the legends suggest. But for those within easy driving, or even walking, distance of one another there were small parties where the host barbecued spare ribs and the guests helped themselves to the jambalaya. It was on one of these usually cosy evenings that, as we were leaving, the hostess asked about the losses we had suffered in the fire. We had become fairly used to this. What they really wanted to know was how well we had been insured and how boring we were likely to become with our particular hard-luck story. We had a reassuring message: the government was going to be generous; all losses that were not covered by insurance would be claimed as a deduction from income tax. That satisfied the hostess, but the host thought differently. He was a screenwriter from way back and he had had successful plays on English-speaking stages all over the world; he wasn't a very good writer, to my way of thinking, but he was a pro. He looked past Joan at me. 'It's bad luck about the Thomas Hope sideboard Joan bought last year at Sotheby's,' he said; 'but what about the books you lost? You can deduct their cost, you can buy others, but you can't replace them. You'll have to make a fresh start. Here' – he grabbed a book from the shelf nearest to him – 'you can make a start with this. It's a spare copy. With our love.'

The book was a Roget's Thesaurus, not a reference book I used or liked. I had long ago found that looking in Roget for synonyms or alternative ways of expressing myself was always a strong indication that I did not know what I really wanted to say. A good dictionary was more conducive to clarity. Roget was for crossword-puzzle compilers and business conference speech-writers.

He meant well, I'm sure, and a polite smile with my thanks would have been a reasonable response. Instead, I burst into tears. They did not last long but it was all most embarrassing. Years later the man with the spare Roget told me that at that moment he had written me off as a writer, that I had become a casualty in the good old Hollywood crack-up tradition.

Joan, charitably, put my lapse down to the drinks we had had before going to the party. Though she was indeed mourning the loss of the Thomas Hope sideboard she was much more deeply hurt by the loss of her family papers and other personal things. I understood. Books, after all, could be replaced; and it wasn't as if I had collected rare books or first editions.

Indeed it wasn't, and I was as puzzled as she was. What I kept recalling, though, was the time before the war, twenty years or more earlier, when I had taken pride in my state of having no personal possessions except a dictionary, a foolscap pad or two, a pencil sharpener and a suitcase. I was back to that state now. What was there to snivel about?

In London I began to think about *The Light of Day* again, but not with the idea of recalling and reproducing what I had written before.

I have never really planned a book, certainly not on paper; I have usually seen it first, hazily, as a journey to be made by characters who are all regurgitated and reassembled bits of me. Sometimes, as the journey progresses, I get tired of it. If the characters fail to live up to their promise, even after much rewriting, and the telling of the story becomes laboured, I discard the whole project. The decision to do so is not taken lightly and, lest I should at some later date weaken and try to revive a duck already pronounced dead, I have usually destroyed the manuscript.

Now, the decision to destroy had been made for me and although the duck was undoubtedly dead, I did not like the way it had died. If there was any killing of that sort to be done, I liked to do it myself. Naturally I looked for someone to blame, someone to punish. I found only myself, the crass believer in fairy tales, the clown who bought fireproof safes. Very well! The clown must suffer the humiliation he so richly deserved. *The Light of Day* would rise again but it would become an autobiographical novel and, worse, a comedy.

Arthur Abdel Simpson, pimp, pander, guide, pornographer and sneak thief was my stand-in for the part of the clown hero and he served me well. Of course, I am not the first writer to work his way out of depression by turning to comedy, but I have been one of the lucky ones. Readers of genre fiction do not like a writer with whom they have come to feel safe suddenly changing his tone of voice. Normally friendly reviewers were inclined to dismiss *The Light of Day* as an aberration. In Europe, however, I gained readers. The book was made into a successful film called *Topkapi* with Peter Ustinov playing my egregious Arthur Abdel Simpson and winning an Oscar for the performance. It was the film that sold the book in France and Italy.

We built a new house with a flat roof and a small swimming pool which could be pumped into our own fire hoses next time we had a fire. I used to test the system once a month. The house was all right, but we never liked it as much as we had liked the old one. We began to travel more, inside the United States on film business, outside to see and smell the less well-travelled countries of northern South America: Surinam, Guyana and Venezuela. We were in Georgetown, Guyana when Sir Winston Churchill died and we were among those who signed the condolence book put up in a sentry box outside Government House. As a result we were invited to an evening of one-act plays given by the Georgetown Little Theatre Club. The Government House information officer was a member.

It was a fascinating occasion. Guyana, which has a multi-racial population, was learning to live with political independence just then and not finding it easy. There were two major ethnic groups: the black descendants of African slaves and the brown descendants of indentured Indian labourers brought in by the British when slavery became illegal. During the hundred years since then the two groups had lived and developed separately. The African blacks had taken to the professions and become the country's doctors, lawyers and administrators; the Indians had made business and money-making their special concerns. The blacks were mostly Christ-ian and the court lawyers among them, the judges and barristers, wore wigs like their Inns of Court brethren. The browns were mostly Hindu and on their houses flew flags to the greater glory of mother India, though none of them had ever been there. The suburbs of Georgetown in which these two 'majorities' lived were all adjacent. A British army peace-keeping force had had to be called in to stop the fighting and

killing. The police force was more of a gendarmerie with
members of the Portuguese and Chinese minorities represented in it, and even, it was said, a few British. Guyana was a
big country and the mountainous interior with its rain forests
was still largely unexplored. A border dispute with Venezuela
had been going on for sixty years or more. There was diamond
mining up there near the frontier. The dispute would go on for
another sixty years.

The Little Theatre Club presented four plays that evening.
Two had been selected from the Samuel French catalogue of
one-act plays available for licensing by amateur groups; the
other two were by local writers and being performed for the
first time. One of the published plays was by Emlyn Williams
and at first I hoped to use that production as a measure of
theatrical effectiveness with which to assess the others. It was
an early play and was about the struggle of a young man to break
his emotional ties with and get away from the Welsh village in
which he had been born. I recognized the theme; it was about
Emlyn as a young man long before he wrote *The Corn is Green*.
True, it was odd to see and hear a railway stationmaster in rural
Wales played by a Chinese and his wayward son played by a
black African twice his size, but it all seemed to work in the
theatre. So did the other three plays. The trouble was that they
all had the same theme: everyone with roots in Georgetown
wanted to get away from them. The plays they chose to perform
were either foreign parables based on that theme or bold local
expressions of it. It could have been monotonous, but the
casting was so eccentric that the plays held you. Most amateur
theatricals tend to have difficulty casting some parts. In
Georgetown they seemed to have none. If the actor could read
the part satisfactorily he or she was given it, regardless of race,
colour, shape or size. There might be racial strife in the suburbs
but in the Georgetown Little Theatre the harmony was
impressive.

After the show there was a big party to which we were
invited. The hostess was a remarkably beautiful young black
woman who was the director and presiding genius of the Little
Theatre. The party was in her rather splendid house; her
husband was young, white and a senior manager in the
Georgetown off-shoot of a Caribbean trading company with

115

roots in London. I congratulated him on the evening and his house. He nodded glumly and glanced across at his wife dazzling the other end of the room. 'She does a wonderful job,' he said, 'but we'd like to get out.'

'Of this house?' Joan and I were in the flimsy squalor of the Park Hotel.

'No, out of Guyana.' It was like a scene from one of the plays. 'There's no future here. Surely that's obvious.'

'Where would you go? Back to England?'

'God no. We want to go to the States.'

'Whereabouts there?'

He took me aside and handed me another drink. 'Well, I've done business with a lot of auto people there, people like Ford and General Motors. We rather fancy Detroit. You live and work in America, what do you think?'

I thought quickly and rather desperately. This was in the mid-sixties. Martin Luther King had had a dream and the civil rights movement was making steady progress; but the progress had been chiefly in the other Southern states where the reaction against it had been most violent. If he had proposed Los Angeles I could have said with some confidence that San Francisco might be a better choice, or better still, Seattle; General Motors had a truck plant up there and a white English businessman with an intelligent black Guyanan wife might well be an acceptable social novelty. About Detroit I just didn't know. So what I said, lamely, was that in his place I would go to Detroit and find out for myself what the job prospects were like for alien managers.

Joan was amazed when I told her about it later.

'They're not going anywhere,' she said; 'that house goes with his job, she told me. Besides they wouldn't be allowed to take any money out. Seattle? They're not crazy up there. They might take her, or him, but not him and her. They're better off here. Here, as long as she's with him, he'll be all right.'

Once, going through immigration at LA airport on our way home, we were stopped by a supervising official who looked again at our passports and the Green Cards confirming our status as resident aliens. She was large, black and had a well-educated voice.

'Mrs Ambler, you've been resident since 'thirty-eight. Mr

116

Ambler, you've been resident since 'fifty-eight. You've been here long enough. How come you haven't applied for citizenship? Can't you make up your minds or don't you care?

Joan said something about our not getting round to it. We were dismissed with a cold nod. She knew as well as we did that for UK British passport-holders who paid their US taxes and social security, citizenship was not important. One couldn't vote in elections, of course, but we had shaken hands with Lyndon B. Johnson and said 'hello' to Richard M. Nixon, and so had no desire to vote. Unless one was very rich indeed and into oil and cattle in such a big way that one could make a few extra millions legally out of depletion allowances, there was not much point in being a citizen. Naturally, if one came from a Central American sugar republic or Eastern Europe or some place like North Vietnam, things were different.

For safe drivers in California periodic renewal of a driving licence is almost automatic; almost, but not quite. There is an eyesight test and, much to my surprise, there came a day when I failed the test. Thereafter I had to wear glasses. I also had to learn to type. Years of writing and rewriting by hand had done peculiar things to some bones in my neck. It had become painful to use the right hand. I wrote the whole of one novel laboriously with my left. There was a chiropractor named Doc Mitchell at the MGM studios to whom I became addicted. Joan was tired of making television and wanted to return to films. The best English-speaking films were now being made in Europe. As a student Joan had been to the Sorbonne as well as Oxford. We were both nearing sixty. It was time, perhaps, for us to look for fresh fields.

'The Blood Bargain' was one of the things that I wrote with my left hand. It began as a political thriller with a Central American setting and as an experiment. In the old days it would have been destroyed when it failed to develop. After the fire I had become more careful. When a London editor, George Hardinge, wrote asking for a short story that had not been published before, I had another look at the experiment and found that I still liked ex-President Fuentes. Spanish America has had too many military dictators. Fuentes is a crook, of course, but he is not a monster; nor would he ever have become one. He is a liar, a cheat, a politician and a good family man.

The Blood Bargain

Ex-President Fuentes enjoys a peculiar distinction. More people would like to kill him now that he is in retirement than wanted to kill him when he was in power.

He is a puzzled and indignant man.

What he fails to understand is that, while men like General Perez may in time forgive you for robbing them, they will never forgive you for making them look foolish.

The *coup d'état* that overthrew Fuentes' Social Action Party government was well organized and relatively bloodless.

The leaders of the *coup* were mostly Army officers, but they had understandings with fellow-dissidents in the Air Force and Navy as well as the discreet blessing of the Church. A price for the collaboration of the Chief of Police had been agreed upon well in advance, and the lists of certain left-wing deputies, militant trade union officials, pro-government newspaper editors, Castro-trained subversives, and other undesirables whose prompt arrest would be advisable, had been compiled with his help. Similar arrangements had been made in the larger provincial towns. Although the conspirators were by no means all of the same political complexion, they had for once found themselves able to sink their differences in the pursuit of a common goal. Whatever might come afterwards, they were all agreed upon one thing; if the country were to be saved from corruption, Communist subversion, anarchy, bankruptcy, civil war, and, ultimately, foreign military intervention, President Fuentes had to go.

One evening in September he went.

The tactics employed by the 'Liberation Front' conspirators followed the pattern that has become more or less traditional when a *coup* is backed by organized military forces and

118

opposed, if it is opposed at all, only by civilian mobs and confused, lightly armed garrison units.

As darkness fell, the tanks of two armoured brigades together with trucks containing a parachute regiment, signals units, and a company of combat engineers rolled into the capital. Within little more than an hour, they had secured their major objectives. Meanwhile, the Air Force had taken over the international airport, grounded all planes, and established a headquarters in the customs and immigration building. An infantry division now began to move into the city and take up positions that would enable it to deal with the civil disturbances that were expected to develop as news of the *coup*, and of the mass arrests that were accompanying it, reached the densely populated slum areas with their high concentration of Fuentes supporters.

A little after eight thirty a squadron of tanks and a special task force of paratroopers reached the Presidential Palace. The palace guard resisted for a quarter of an hour and suffered casualties of eight wounded. The order to surrender was given personally to the guard commander by President Fuentes 'in order to avoid further bloodshed'.

When this was reported to General Perez, the leader of the *coup*, he drove to the Palace. He was accompanied by five senior members of the Liberation Front council, including the Chief of Police, and no less than three representatives of the foreign press. The latter had been flushed out of the Jockey Club bar by an aide earlier in the evening and hastily briefed on the aims and ideals of the Liberation Front. General Perez wished to lose no time in establishing himself abroad as a magnanimous, reasonable, and responsible man, and his regime as worthy of prompt diplomatic recognition.

The newsmen's accounts of the interview between President Fuentes and General Perez, and of the now-notorious 'blood bargain' that emerged from it, were all in substantial agreement. At the time the bargain seemed to them just another of those civilized, oddly chivalrous agreements to live and let live which, by testifying to the continued presence of compassion and good sense even at moments of turmoil and destruction, have so often lightened the long, dark history of Latin American revolution. The reporters, all experienced men, can scarcely be blamed for misunderstanding it. They knew, as everyone else knew, that President Fuentes was a devious and deeply dishonest man. The only mistake they made was in assuming that the other parties to the bargain had made due allowance for that deviousness and dishonesty and knew exactly what they were doing. What the reporters had not realized was that these normally wary and hard-headed officers had become so intoxicated by the speed and extent of their initial success that by the time they reached the Presidential Palace they were no longer capable of thinking clearly.

President Fuentes received General Perez and the other Liberation Front leaders in the ornate Cabinet Room of the Palace to which he had been taken by the paratroopers who had arrested him. With him were the other male occupants of the Presidential air raid shelter at the time of his arrest. These included the Palace guard commander, the President's valet, the Palace major domo, two footmen and the man who looked after the Palace plumbing system, in addition to the Minister of Public Welfare, the Minister of Agrarian Education, the Minister of Justice, and the elderly Controller of the Presidential Secretariat. The Minister of Public Welfare had brought a bottle of brandy with him from the shelter and smiled glassily throughout the subsequent confrontation. Agrarian Education and Justice maintained expressions of bewilderment and indignation, but confined their oral protests to circumspect murmurs. The thin-lipped young captain in charge of the paratroopers handled his machine pistol as if he would have been glad of an excuse to use it.

Only the President seemed at ease. There was even a touch of impatience in the shrug with which he rose to face General Perez and his party as they strode in from the anteroom; it was as if he had been interrupted by some importunate visitor during a game of bridge.

His calm was only partly assumed. He knew all about General Perez's sensitivity to foreign opinion, and he had immediately recognized the newsmen in the rear of the procession. They would not have been brought there if any immediate violence to his person had been contemplated.

The impatience he displayed was certainly genuine; it was impatience with himself. He had known for weeks that a *coup* was in preparation, and had taken the precaution a month earlier of sending his wife and children and his mistress out of the country. They were all now in Washington, and he had planned, using as a pretext his announced wish to address personally a meeting of the Organization of American States, to join them there the following week. His private spies had reported that the *coup* would undoubtedly be timed to take advantage of his absence abroad. Since the *coup* by means of which he himself had come to power five years earlier had been timed in that way, he had been disposed to believe the report.

Now, he knew better. Whether or not his spies had deliberately deceived him did not matter at the moment. A mistake had been made which was, he knew, likely to cost him more than temporary inconvenience. Unless he could retrieve it immediately, by getting out of the country within the next few hours, that mistake would certainly cost him his liberty, and most probably his life too.

He had risked death before, was familiar with the physical and mental sensations that accompanied the experience, and with a small effort was able to ignore them. As General Perez came up to him, the President displayed no emotion of any kind. He merely nodded politely and waited for the General to speak.

For a moment the General seemed tongue-tied. He was sweating too. As this was the first time he had overthrown a government he was undoubtedly suffering from stage fright. He took refuge finally in military punctilio. With a click of the heels he came to attention and fixed his eyes on the President's left ear.

'We are here . . . ' he began harshly, then cleared his throat and corrected himself. 'I and my fellow members of the Council of the Liberation Front are here to inform you that a state of national emergency now exists.'

The President nodded politely. 'I am glad to have that information, General. Since telephone communication has been cut off I have naturally been curious as to what was happening. These gentlemen' – he motioned to the paratroopers – 'seemed unwilling to enlighten me.'

The General ignored this and went on as if he were reading a proclamation. In fact he was quoting from the press release which had already been handed to the newsmen. 'Directed by the Council and under its orders,' he said, 'the armed forces have assumed control of all functions of civil government in the state, and, as provided in the Constitution, formally demand your resignation.'

The President looked astounded. 'You have the effrontery to claim constitutional justification for this mutiny?'

For the first time since he had entered the room the General relaxed slighty. 'We have a precedent, Sir. Nobody should know that better than you. You yourself set it when you legalized your own seizure of power from your predecessor. Need I remind you of the wording of the amendment? "If for any reason, including the inability to fulfil the duties of his office by reason of ill health, mental or physical, or absence, an elected president is unable to exercise the authority vested in him under the constitution, a committee representative of the nation and those responsible to it for the maintenance of law and order may request his resignation and be entitled . . . "'

For several seconds the President had been waving his hands for silence. Now he broke in angrily. 'Yes, yes, I know all about that. But my predecessor was absent. I am not. Neither am I ill, physically or mentally. There are no legal grounds on which you are entitled to ask for my resignation.'

'No legal grounds, Sir?' General Perez could smile now. He pointed to the paratroopers. 'Are you able to exercise the authority of a president? *Are* you? If you think so, try.'

The President pretended to think over the challenge. The interview was so far going more or less as he had expected; but the next moves would be the critical ones for him. He walked over to a window and back in order to give himself time to collect himself.

Everyone there was watching him. The tension in the room was mounting. He could feel it. It was odd, he thought. Here he was, a prisoner, wholly at their mercy; and yet they were waiting for him to come to a decision, to make a choice where no choice existed. It was absurd. All they wanted from him was relief from a small and quite irrational sense of guilt. They had the Church's blessing; now the poor fools yearned for the blessing of the law too. Very well. They should have it. But it would be expensive.

He turned and faced General Perez again.

'A resignation exacted from me under duress would have no force in law,' he said.

The General glanced at the Chief of Police. 'You are a lawyer, Raymundo. Who represents the law here?'

'The Council of the Liberation Front, General.'

Perez looked at the President again. 'You see, Sir, there are no technical difficulties. We even have the necessary document already prepared.'

His aide held up a black leather portfolio.

The President hesitated, looking from one face to another as if hoping against hope that he might find a friendly one. Finally he shrugged. 'I will read the document,' he said coldly and walked towards the cabinet table. As he did so he seemed to become aware again of his fellow prisoners in the room. He stopped suddenly.

'Must my humiliation be witnessed by my colleagues and my servants as well as the foreign press?' he demanded bitterly.

General Perez motioned to the paratrooper captain. 'Take those men into another room. Leave guards outside the doors of this one.'

The President waited until the group from the air raid shelter had been herded out, then sat down at the table. The General's aide opened the portfolio, took out a legal document laced with green ribbon and placed it in front of the President.

He made a show of studying the document very carefully. In fact, he was indifferent to its contents. His intention was simply to let the tension mount a little further and to allow the other men there to feel that they were on the point of getting what they wanted.

For three minutes there was dead silence in the room. It was broken only by the sound of distant machine-gun fire. It seemed to be coming from the south side of the city. The President heard a slight stir from the group of men behind him and one of them cleared his throat nervously. There was another burst of firing. The President took no notice of it. He read the document through a third time then put it down and sat back in his chair.

The aide offered him a pen with which to sign. The President ignored it and turned his head so that he could see General Perez.

'You spoke of a resignation, General,' he said. 'You did not mention that it was to be a confession also.'

'Hardly a confession, Sir,' the General replied drily. 'We would not expect you voluntarily to incriminate yourself. The admission is only of incompetence. That is not yet a criminal offence in a head of state.'

The President smiled faintly. 'And if I were to sign this paper, what kind of personal treatment might I expect to receive afterwards? A prison cell perhaps, with a carefully staged treason trial to follow? Or merely a bullet in the head and an unmarked grave?'

The General reddened. 'We are here to correct abuses of power, sir, not to imitate them. When you have signed you will be conducted to your former home in Alazan province. You will be expected to remain there for the present and the Governor of the province will be instructed to see that you do so. Apart from that restriction you will be free to do as you please. Your family will naturally be permitted to join you.'

'You mention the house in Alazan province. What about my other personal property?'

'You will be permitted to retain everything you owned when you took office.'

'I see.' The President stood up and moved away from the table. 'I will think about it. I will let you have my decision tomorrow,' he added casually.

The silence that followed this announcement did not last long, but one of the newsmen reported later that it was one of the loudest he had ever heard. Another remembered that during it he suddenly became conscious of the presence and smell of a large bowl of tropical flowers on a side table by the ante-room door.

The President had walked towards the windows again. General Perez took two steps towards him, then stopped.

'You must decide at once! You must sign now!' he snapped.

The President turned on him. 'Why? Why now?'

It was the Chief of Police who answered him. 'Son of a whore, because we tell you to!' he shouted.

Suddenly they were all shouting at him. One officer was so

enraged that he drew his pistol. The General had difficulty in restoring order.

The President took no notice of them. He kept his eyes on General Perez, but it was really the newsmen he was addressing now. As the din subsided he raised his voice.

'I asked a question, General. Why now? Why the haste? It is a reasonable question. If, as you say, you already control the country, what have you to fear from me? Or is it, perhaps, that your control is not in fact as complete and effective as you would have us believe?'

The General had to quell another angry outburst from his colleagues before he could answer, but he preserved his own temper admirably. His reply was calm and deliberate.

'I will tell you exactly what we control so that you may judge for yourself,' he said. 'To begin with, all provincial army garrisons, air force establishments, and police posts have declared for the Liberation Front, as have five out of eight of the provincial governors. The three objectors – I am sure you will have guessed who they are – have been rendered harmless and replaced by military governors. None of this can come as a great surprise to you, I imagine. You never had much support outside the capital and the mining areas.'

The President nodded. 'Stupidity can sometimes be charted geographically,' he remarked.

'Now as to the capital. We control the airfields, both military and civil, the naval base, all communications including telephone and radio and television broadcast facilities, the power stations, all fuel oil storage facilities, all main traffic arteries, all government offices and city police posts together with the offices and printing presses of El Correo and La Gaceta.' He glanced at his watch. 'In connection with the broadcast facilities, I may mention that while the television station is temporarily off the air, the radio station will shortly begin broadcasting an announcement of the establishment of the new Liberation Front regime, which I recorded two days ago. As I told you before, everything is now under our control.'

The President smiled and glanced significantly at the newsmen. 'Are the *sumideri* under control, General?'

Sumideri, meaning sinks or drains, was the popular slang

term used to describe the slum areas on the south side of the capital.

The General hesitated only an instant. 'The southern area is effectively contained,' he replied stiffly. 'The first infantry division reinforced by the third tank brigade has that responsibility.'

'I see.' The President looked again at the newsmen. 'So the civil war may be expected to begin at any moment.'

With a quick motion of his hands the General silenced the chorus of objections from his colleagues. 'We are fully prepared to deal firmly with any mob violence which may occur,' he said. 'Of that you may be sure.'

'Yes,' said the President bitterly, 'perhaps civil war is not the phrase to use for the planned massacre of unarmed civilians.' He swung around suddenly to face the newsmen and his voice hardened. 'You have been witnesses to this farce, gentlemen. I ask you to remember it well and let the civilized world know of it. These men come to ask for my resignation as head of state. That is all they want! Why? Because outside in the streets of the city their tanks and guns are waiting to begin the slaughter of the thousands of men and women who will protest their loyalty to me. And the way to bring them out for the slaughter is to fling my resignation like so much filth in their faces!

General Perez could stand it no longer. 'That is a lie!' he shouted.

The President turned on him savagely. 'Do you think they will *not* come out? Why else are they "contained" as you call it? Why else? Because they are my people and because they will listen only to me.'

A glow of triumph suffused General Perez' angry face. 'Then their blood will be on *your* hands!' he roared. He stabbed a forefinger at the newsmen. 'You heard what he said, gentlemen. *They do what he tells them!* It is his responsibility, then, not ours, if they oppose us. *He* will be the murderer of women and children! Let him deny it.'

This time the President made no reply. He just stood there looking about him in bewilderment, like a boxer who has staggered to his feet after a count of ten and can't quite realize that the fight is over. At last he walked slowly back to the cabinet table, sat down heavily, and buried his head in his hands.

Nobody else moved. When the President raised his head and looked at them again his eyes were haggard. He spoke very quietly.

'You are right,' he said, 'they are my people and they will do as I tell them. It is my responsibility. I accept it. There must be no senseless bloodshed. I think it is my duty to tell them not to protest.'

For a moment they all stared at him incredulously. The Chief of Police started to say something, then stopped as he caught General Perez' eye. If the man were serious this was too good an opportunity to miss.

General Perez went over and addressed the President. 'I cannot believe that even you would speak lightly on such a matter, but I must ask if you seriously mean what you say?'

The President nodded absently. 'I will need about an hour to draft my statement. There is a direct line to the radio station here in the Palace and the necessary equipment. The station can record me on tape.' He managed a rueful smile. 'In the circumstances, I imagine that you would prefer a recording to a live broadcast.'

'Yes.' But the General was still reluctant to believe in his triumph. 'How can you be sure that they will obey you?' he asked.

The President thought before he answered. 'There will be some, of course, who will be too distressed, too angry perhaps, to do as I ask,' he said. 'But if the officers commanding troops are ordered to use restraint, casualties can be kept to a minimum.' He glanced at the Chief of Police. 'There should be moderation, too, in respect of arrests. But the majority will listen to me, I think.' He paused. 'The important thing is that they must believe that I am speaking as a free man, and not out of fear because there is a pistol at my head.'

'I myself can give them that assurance,' said the General. The fact that he could make such an ingenuous suggestion is an indication of his mental confusion at that point.

The President raised his eyebrows. 'With all respect, General, I don't think we could expect them at this time to believe you of all people. I also think that the news that I am to be kept under what amounts to house arrest in Alazan province will not help to convince them either.'

'Then what do you propose? You can scarcely remain here in the capital.'

'Naturally not.' The President sat back in his chair. He had assumed a statesmanlike air now. 'It is quite clear,' he said, 'that we must achieve an orderly and responsible transfer of power. I shall, of course, resign in order to make way for the Liberation Front. However, in your place, I must say that I would regard my continued presence anywhere in this country as undesirable. These people to whom I am to appeal tonight will only respond with restraint because of their loyalty to me. That loyalty will continue as long as they are able to give expression to it. You would do better really to get rid of me. As soon as I have spoken to my people you should get me out of the country as quickly as you can.'

'Exile?' It was the Chief of Police who spoke up now. 'But if we exile you that looks no better than house arrest in Alazan. Worse, possibly.'

'Exactly.' The President nodded approvingly. 'The solution I suggest is that I am permitted to announce to my people that I will continue to serve them, the nation, and the Liberation Front, but in a different capacity and abroad. Our embassy in Nicaragua is without an ambassador at present. That would be a suitable appointment. I suggest that after I have recorded my broadcast I leave the country immediately in order to take up my post.'

The council discussion that ensued lacked the vehemence of the earlier exchanges. The strain of the past twenty-four hours was beginning to tell on General Perez and his colleagues; they were getting tired; and the sounds of firing from the south side were becoming more insistent. Time was running out. It was one of the newsmen who drew their attention to the fact.

'General,' he said to Perez, 'has it occurred to you that if the President doesn't talk to these people of his pretty soon they're all going to be out on the streets anyway?'

The President recognized the urgency, too, but refused to be hurried. As he pointed out, there were matters of protocol to be dealt with before he could make his appeal to the people. For one thing, his resignation would have to be redrafted. Since, he argued, he was now to be appointed his country's Ambassador to Nicaragua, references in the present draft to his incompetence would obviously have to be deleted. And there were other clauses which might be interpreted as reflections on his personal integrity.

In the end, the President wrote his own act of resignation. It was a simple document but composed with great care. His radio speech, on the other hand, he scribbled out on a cabinet desk pad while technicians, hastily summoned by jeep from the central radio building, were setting up a recording circuit in the anteroom.

Meanwhile, telephone communication had been restored to the Palace, and the Controller of the Presidential Secretariat had been released from arrest and put to work in his office.

His first task had been to contact the Nicaraguan Ambassador, give him a discreetly censored account of the current situation and request him to ascertain immediately, in accordance with Article 8 of the Pan-American Convention, if his government would be prepared to accept ex-President Fuentes as *persona grata* in the capacity of ambassador to their country. The Nicaraguan Ambassador had undertaken to telephone personally to the Minister of Foreign Relations in Managua and report back. His unofficial opinion was that there would be no opposition to the proposed appointment.

With the help of the air force council member present the Controller next spoke to the officer in charge at the International Airport. He learned that of the two civil airliners grounded earlier that evening, one had been southbound to Caracas, the other, a Colombian Avianca jet, had been northbound to Mexico City. Fortunately, a Vice-Consul from the Colombian Consulate-General was already at the airport, having been summoned there by the Avianca captain to protest the grounding. The Controller spoke with the Vice-Consul who said that Avianca would be willing to carry ex-President Fuentes as a passenger to Mexico City if the Mexican Government would permit him to land. A call to the Mexican Embassy explaining that ex-President Fuentes would be in transit through Mexican territory on his way to his post as an accredited diplomatic representative to the republic of Nicaragua secured the necessary permission.

The President already had a diplomatic passport which needed only minor amendments to fit it for its new role. All that was needed now to facilitate his departure was confirmation from the Nicaraguan Ambassador that he would be accorded diplomatic status in Managua. Within an hour, the Nicaraguan Government, acting promptly in the belief that they were helping both parties to the arrangement, had replied favourably.

The escape route was open.

President Fuentes made two tape-recordings of the appeal to his supporters, one for the radio, the second for use by a loudspeaker van in the streets of the *sumideri*. Then he signed his resignation and was driven to the airport. General Perez provided an escort of armoured cars.

The plane, with ex-President Fuentes on board, took off a little after midnight. Five hours later it landed in Mexico City.

News of the Liberation Front *coup* and of the President's voluntary resignation and ambassadorial appointment had been carried by all the international wire services, and there were reporters waiting for him. There was also, despite the early hour, a protocol official from the Department of External Relations to meet him. Fuentes made a brief statement to the reporters, confirming the fact of his resignation. On the subject of his appointment as Ambassador to Nicaragua he was vague. He then drove to a hotel in the city. On the way there he asked the protocol official if it would be convenient for him to call upon the Minister of External Affairs later that day.

The official was mildly surprised. As Ambassador Fuentes was merely passing through Mexico, a brief note of thanks to the Minister would normally be the only courtesy expected of him. On the other hand, the circumstances of Fuentes' sudden translation from President to Ambassador were unusual and it was possible that the Minister might be glad of the opportunity of hearing what Fuentes himself had to say on the subject. He promised that he would consult the Minister's personal assistant at the earliest possible moment.

The Minister received Ambassador Fuentes at five o'clock that afternoon.

The two men had met before, at conferences of the Organization of American States and on the occasion of a state visit to

Mexico paid by Fuentes soon after he became President. It was a tribute to the Minister's natural courtesy as well as his self-discipline that Fuentes believed that the Minister liked him. In fact the Minister viewed him with dislike and disapproval and had not been in the least surprised or distressed by the news of the Liberation Front *coup*. However, he had been amused by Fuentes' ability to emerge from the situation not only alive and free but also invested with diplomatic immunity; and it modified his distaste for the man. He was, one had to admit, an engaging scoundrel.

After the preliminary politenesses had been disposed of the Minister inquired courteously whether he could be of any service to the Ambassador during his stay in Mexico.

Fuentes inclined his head: 'That is most kind of you, Mr Minister,' he said graciously. 'Yes, there is one thing.'

'You only have to ask.'

'Thank you.' Ambassador Fuentes straightened up a little in his chair. 'I wish,' he said, 'to make formal application to be considered here as a refugee, and formally to request political asylum in the United States of Mexico.'

The Minister stared for a moment, then smiled.

'Surely you must be joking, Mr Ambassador.'

'Not in the least.'

The Minister was puzzled, and because he was puzzled he put into words the first obvious objection that came into his head.

'But in the United States of Mexico, even though you are not accredited to the Federal Government, you already, by virtue of the Pan-American Convention, enjoy diplomatic status and privileges here,' he said.

It was a statement which he was later to regret.

Ambassador Fuentes never took up his post in Nicaragua.

One of the first official acts of General Perez's Council of the Liberation Front was to set up a committee, headed by the Professor of Political Economy at Bolívar University, to report on the financial state of the Republic.

It took the committee only a few days to discover that during the past three years ex-President Fuentes had authorized printings of five hundred peseta banknotes to a total value of one hundred million dollars and that twenty of those hundred millions could not be accounted for.

The Governor of the National Bank was immediately arrested. He was an old man who had spent most of his life in the National Archives gathering material for a scholarly study of colonial Spanish land grants. He had been appointed to the bank by Fuentes. He knew nothing about banking. He had merely carried out the orders of the Minister of Finance.

Fuentes had been his own Minister of Finance.

Interviewed on the subject by the press in Mexico City, ex-President Fuentes stated that the committee's revelations had shocked, horrified, and amazed him. He also said that he had no idea where the missing twenty million might be. Regrettably, he was unable quite to refrain from smiling as he said it.

Ex-President Fuentes' retirement has not been peaceful.

During the five years he held office as President there was only one serious attempt on his life. Since he resigned the Presidency, ceased to concern himself with politics, and went to live abroad, no less than three such attempts have been made. There will doubtless be others. Meanwhile, he has had to fight off two lots of extradition proceedings and a number of civil actions directed against his European bank accounts.

He is wealthy, of course, and can afford to pay for the protection, both physical and legal, that he needs; but he is by no means resigned to the situation. As he is fond of pointing out, other men in his position have accumulated larger fortunes. Moreover, his regime was never unacceptably oppressive. He was no Trujillo, no Batista, no Porfirio Diaz. Why then should he be hounded and harassed as if he were?

Ex-President Fuentes remains a puzzled and indignant man.

To be continued

From California we went to live in French-speaking Switzerland.

Clarens, our resting place, is on the north shore of Lac Léman and at the far end of the lake away from Geneva in the canton of Vaud, once in the middle ages the territory of the Counts (Vert et Rouge) of Savoy. It was these counts who built the castles of Chillon and La Tour-de-Peilz to protect their lands from the savagery of the barbarian mountain tribe who came from the region which is now described as the canton of Berne and the Berner Oberland. Berne and its agents, the bishops of Berne and Sion, stayed for two hundred years until, to quote a local historian, 'Ce fut enfin, en 1798, la révolution vaudoise. Le Pays de Vaud devint un canton suisse et reste un pays.'

However, ten years went by before the Bernois could be persuaded to recognize Vaud's independence as a canton and it took Napoleon to enforce the separation. The Helvetic tribes had always been jealous of territorial boundaries. Even the Roman legions, tough customers themselves, had found it easier in the end to bypass Helvetic lands than to face the trials of marching through them. For foreigners like Joan and me Berne was the federal capital, a place of embassies and consulate-generals and a place worth visiting for the pictures in its fine art gallery. For the Vaudois, however, the word Berne was also a reminder of things past. The local garage man told me of this without really meaning to do so. I had ordered a new car from him, but until it was delivered I was driving rental cars which I picked up at Geneva airport. Our furniture and other belongings were still at sea in a container ship and, while Joan completed her work on a film she was making at Paramount, I commuted between London and Clarens. The offending car was the third I had rented and I did not even know what make it was. I had stopped at the garage to top up with petrol and to find out when my own car would be delivered; I had made the mistake of ordering an extra – real leather on the seats. I was given no chance to ask questions: the *garagiste* came out of his office to greet me the moment I stopped. 'Ah, monsieur,' he cried, 'vous êtes bernois maintenant.'

He was smiling broadly when he said it. Clearly there was a joke here that I did not understand. I asked him what it was. He pointed to the registration plates on the rental car. Except for transients with TT plates car registrations were always cantonal. BE stood for Berne. I liked the *garagiste*. We were about the same age and he had done his military service in the artillery. In his lapel he wore a small enamel badge with the silhouette of a field gun. It could have been a miniature version of the Royal Artillery cap badge I had worn during my military service. I had also served for a time with a regiment from Ulster and learned to take a hint about the odd quirk or prejudice without asking stupid questions. In Vaud a foreigner was better off driving a car with French-speaking plates; or Italian, or British.

With tourists the Vaudois are infinitely patient. From foreigners intending to live in the canton, however, they require respect for local sensibilities. When I went to buy light bulbs at the local Uniprix – no tourist buys sixty-watt light bulbs – the stern matriarch at the check-out till corrected me sharply when in counting out some small change, I used the words quartre-vingts-dix for ninety.

'Non, monsieur, non. Ici nous sommes suisse et vaudois. Les français disent quatre-vingts-dix. Bien. Ils sont français. Ici nous sommes vaudois et nous disons "nonante". C'est beaucoup plus simple. D'accord?'

'D'accord, madame.' For her, after all, the *révolution* of 1789 had been *vaudoise*. After that, I said *huitante* and *nonante* with everyone else.

Seen from a passing car on the main road just above it, the harbour of Clarens is unusually attractive. Most lakeside yachting marinas are bleak places out of season or in bad weather when the dinghy-class sails are furled and the ten metre plutocrats are stuffing themselves with beef fondue in their cabins. Clarens was different. Storms on Lac Léman can be sudden, violent and dangerous for any vessel smaller than a broad-beamed steamer. The year we arrived an excursion boat from the French side was capsized by a squall. Among the drowned was a party of school children on a holiday outing. Clarens has one of the few safe harbours on the north shore. One of the reaons for the safety is the Ile de Salagnon, a small off-shore island with a few poplar trees and an Italian style villa on it and a decrepit boat house. Nobody lived in the villa which was said to be owned by a rich Zuricher and infested with rats. Rats notwithstanding, the island shelters the entrance to the harbour which lies between the stone quay of the marina, now called the Port du Basset, and the steep headland which gives shelter to the west. On the Port du Basset side there is a clutter of chandlers' stores, sail lofts and work sheds which service the weekend yachtsmen, the racing-dinghy young and the visitors with boats on trailers who pay to have their boats winched in and out of the water. The lake police watch-post is a modern building on the other side of the harbour next to the covered docks where the lake patrol and rescue cutters are kept at the ready. Apart from dashing out to save ham-fisted yachtsmen from death in the summer squalls they monitored the antics of Scandinavian hippies in rented power boats. This was not always easy; the harmless pot-smokers sometimes had LSD trippers with them. LSD, it may be recalled, was first synthesized in Switzerland and its commercial manufacture was controlled by a pharmaceutical concern in Basel. It was no student-lab kitchen LSD they brewed but the real thing.

We had an apartment at Chemin de l'Ile de Salagnon, 1, a small modern building of great charm. Our neighbours in it were a Belgian steel man and his wife and, on the ground floor a Swiss army colonel of engineers, also retired. There are not many colonels in the Swiss army and this one, having spent a lifetime building army barracks and mountain fortifications, was a bit eccentric. He was a keen gardener and while at work liked to wear a red fez with a silk tassel hanging from it. His wife, a handsome and cultivated woman, was also very timid. The colonel had a heart condition. René, the Belgian steel man, did not care for military men; in the First War he had worked as a driver for too many of them. René was one of nature's businessmen. He had five pensions, all from steel companies dealing internationally. He and Yvonne his wife spoke most European languages but the best years of their lives had been spent in a big company apartment on Park Avenue in New York. That, however, had been yesterday. Now they had, with us and monsieur le colonel, a commanding view of the lake and the snow-capped Dents du Midi beyond: picture postcard stuff which we tended to ignore. Nearer, and infinitely more interesting, were the goings-on in the port, the yachts, their owners and the birds: swans, mallard ducks, coots and Bonaparte gulls, which had black triangular markings on their heads which looked like the hat worn by the Emperor on the field of Marengo. At the end of the lake beyond Villefranche there was a broad delta where the young river Rhone, flowing from its headwaters in the high alps, entered Léman. Part of the delta was a water-bird reserve and occasionally we had weird and highly coloured visitors. They were not welcomed; our swans could turn nasty and unless the visitor was very large it could be mobbed by the coots. Coots are not crazy but they often behave as if they were. Bonaparte gulls are very well behaved and do not quarrel and screech like herring gulls. Of course, there are no herring in Léman and no gull is going to get excited about perch fished from that lake. The fillets of perch one gets in the restaurants come from fish farms up in the mountains. Things were different, and possibly better, when the Counts of Savoy spent time in their castles and their servants' farm animals could drink from the lake.

Apart from the stone piers of du Basset and small houses like the one we lived in the harbour has not changed much. It still functions as a place of safety. When, in the 19th century, steamers started carrying passengers around and across the lake the Clarens steamer landing stage was built further along the rue du Lac, nearer the Clarens shops and the new abattoir.

Clarens has not often appeared in the pages of history. Paul Kruger, first president of the Boer Republic of the Transvaal, fled to Clarens on the outbreak of the Boer War and died there in 1904. The Kruger National Park is named for him and so is the gold rand coin. The house he died in, now the *Krugerhaus*, is a stone's throw from the Port du Basset and used to have a plate on the door with instructions to would-be visitors. Perhaps there is still someone there to keep the brass polished. Of much greater interest to me was the mystery of where in Clarens Igor Stravinsky had lived and worked during those splendidly productive years before the First War. There is a photograph of him taken in 1915 in the garden of a villa just along the lake at Ouchy. Also in the photograph are Léonide Massine, Léon Bakst and other Ballets Russes notables; but Stravinsky himself lived in Clarens, either in the rue Gambetta or in part of a large house which is now a private school for girls. At least that was the story until the seventies when the composer died in New York. In Clarens then it was conceded that Stravinsky had had lodgings in several houses in those critical years when he had written *Firebird* and *The Rite of Spring*, but that most of them had probably been in or near the rue Gambetta; near enough anyway, for it had been decided to name a street after him in his honour and, more particularly, the honour of Clarens. There were dozens of rue Gambettas in the region; a rue Stravinsky in Clarens would be a lasting distinction.

It never materialized. The local Stravinsky committee found that Clarens could not change any of its street names without higher municipal authority. The higher authority concerned was Montreux, a parvenu tourist resort built on the detritus of mountain land slippages and already notorious for its second-rate Modern Jazz Quinzaine and its no less nasty Rose d'Or Television Awards Festival. It had lost its casino – totally destroyed by a Yugoslav arsonist who made a daring escape by night train to Italy – and the new international convention centre had yet to be paid for. Avid for any kind of publicity which could bring the place a little cultural respectability they stole Stravinsky's name from Clarens. The rue du Casino in Montreux became the rue Stravinsky.

This disgraceful coup caused lasting ill-feeling in Clarens. If Montreux wanted cheap publicity, it was argued, it had more suitable material right in Montreux and Russian-born material too. Why not a rue Nabokov? The author of *Lolita* had made his home there on the sixth floor of the Palace Hotel. True, he was still alive and of a reclusive disposition, but the change could have been made without his prior knowledge, and then put to

139

him as a surprise present on his next birthday. Or there was
Noël Coward up there in Les Avants; that was municipally
sous-Montreux just as Clarens was. It was Madame Pettiloup,
the grocer, who cleared the air for me on that aspect of the
matter. In Vaud persons honoured with named streets had to
be dead, as dead as Gambetta. Clarens should have put up a
statue or a portrait bust of Stravinsky, the way Vevey was
putting up a statue of Charlie Chaplin, even though he lived at
Corsier, which was sous-Vevey, and was still alive. Did I know
that we had a famous British author living in Clarens? His name
was Cronin, A.J. Cronin, and he was one of her best customers.
He had a very nice house up the road at Baugy; he was very old
though, and did not welcome strangers. Madame Pettiloup was
in her eighties and it seemed likely that Dr Cronin was even
older. Joan had a better time marketing chez Pettiloup than I
did; she was never waited on by Madame Pettiloup herself,
always by one of her young and cheerfully efficient daughters-
in-law.

For a dozen or more years we travelled, we explored, we
worked and we enjoyed the company of friends. Of course,
Joan's work took her often away from the Ile de Salagnon. I had
an easier passage. During our years in Switzerland I wrote five
novels and learned a lot about publishing in Europe that I had
not known before. My first good French translator was a
Parisian who later brought his family to live in Clarens. My
German language publisher, Daniel Keel, lives and works in
Zürich. He and his wife Anna remain valued friends.

Our immediate neighbours in Clarens, René and Yvonne
Thieren, were charming people and we used to enjoy our
occasional expeditions with them. These were nearly always to
good restaurants in or near Geneva where René had contacts
from bygone days when he had been a steel executive. French
wines are dutiable in Switzerland but the frontier between
France and the Swiss canton of Geneva is almost impossible to
patrol effectively. There is, or used to be, a going rate for duty-
free vintage champagne of the better marques. René knew that
market. We used to drive to the restaurant where there would
be a table reserved for lunch. Our car would be left outside.
After an excellent lunch and a brief chat about money with the
proprietor of the place we would drive back to Clarens with six

cases of champagne in the boot. René and Yvonne would take four, we would take two. Our garages below the house both had inner doorways leading to our air-raid-shelter-cum-cellar area, and we had a porter's trolley. The only difficulty about these outings was the matter of whose car we went in.

René, though a good man in other respects, was a really bad driver. He liked big powerful American cars and he drove competitively as well as dangerously. He jumped red lights and hooted impatiently if the driver in front seemed to him excessively cautious. He shouted and made insulting gestures. His wife, Yvonne, though a relentless back-seat driver, could do nothing to restrain him; he seemed not to hear a word she said. She sat in a back seat because she preferred it to the front; her family in Belgium had a title of some sort and she had been brought up to sit in the back seat of a landaulette and give instructions to the chauffeur through a speaking tube. Unfortunately she had never lost the habit. When I was the driver and she was in the back with Joan the monologue continued. With me, however, she did not have to order prudence; with me she became a lane changer and a tailgater ('Quick, Eric, he will get through on the yellow'); but that was better than René's awful thrusting.

Of course, he had a lot of accidents, some of them quite serious. That was why he changed his car so often and was always having to pass more driving tests. But in only one accident was he injured badly enough to need a few days in hospital. That was how it was discovered that he had a bowel cancer. He was well into his eighties; he came through the first operation quite successfully, bought a newer, more powerful Buick and took me for a demonstration ride in it. I returned pale and shaken and although it was early in the day had a brandy. Joan predicted that René would soon have another accident and lose his driving licence permanently. She was wrong; it was the cancer that defeated him eventually.

Quite suddenly, it seemed, family and friends were dying off as if a plague had descended on us. Joan and I spent weeks inspecting private nursing homes in South East England looking for one in which my mother could spend her 87th year in reasonable comfort. We found one eventually that was just good enough, but my mother did not last the year. Joan's mother was the next to go, in her one hundredth year. It was after that funeral, when Joan was staying with her sister's family in Iver Heath, that René died in the hospital at Montreux.

I was writing a novel called *Doctor Frigo* and wanted no interruptions. Some people are said to enjoy funerals, to find them vaguely comforting. I do not. I either weep and embarrass the other mourners or get seized with a terrible desire to giggle and so offend them. Whether a funeral ends, for me, in tears or sniggers depends to some extent on the deceased, of course; a death in one's family may not always be a matter for unalloyed grief, but is more likely to be a shared grief, the kind we experience most keenly when a creative artist dies, even when his, or her, best days are done. It is when the conceits of the living, especially those of officiating clergy, are suddenly more in evidence than thoughts for the dead that laughter may begin to intrude. René's funeral was a unique experience. Things went wrong right from the start.

Yvonne the chief mourner had no male relatives and so asked me to act as her personal escort. I had expected that one of René's bankers would have been tapped for this duty but Yvonne said no, that René had asked for me. I didn't believe this but it was not something one could argue about. I reported on time and found the other mourners already assembled. Yvonne began issuing orders. The hearse was at the hospital mortuary chapel with the body and all the flowers in it. The cortège would form up there. She would be with me in the following car which also belonged to the undertaker. The other guests would please follow behind us. Right? Then let's go. She was back in Park Avenue.

It was the undertaker who brought her down to earth again. In the Commune of Montreux, he said, it was forbidden for funerals to form processions and travel *en cortège*. The hearse could proceed followed closely by one car only and must travel at normal speeds conforming to the normal traffic regulations. The other mourners must make their own separate ways to the crematorium at Vevey where they would undoubtedly arrive first. Hearses with coffins and flowers were not allowed to use the main roads because they caused obstructions. They must use the secondary roads inland from the lake.

Yvonne said no. It was outrageous. The municipality must change its mind. Did they not know who René was, who she was? René was eighty-six; to deny a man of that age a decent funeral was disgraceful. He would not permit it. They must be told so.

Someone volunteered to call the gendarmerie and ask for a motorcycle escort out of Montreux. The undertaker said that the law was the same in Vevey. Yvonne poured herself a stiff whisky and sat down defiantly to wait. The undertaker spoke up again. Madame did not perhaps realize that the Vevey crematorium was a very busy place and that an appointment had to be made in advance. If that appointment were not kept that place on the list was forfeited. The hearse itself would even be needed for another funeral later on. He looked at his watch and then, appealingly, at the rest of us.

Yvonne drew in a deep breath. 'Then,' she said, 'let the coffin with my René be taken back to the hospital chapel. Then, we shall decide what to do.'

The undertaker drew breath too, and went to the telephone. The man who had talked to the gendarmerie crept back just then to report failure. The undertaker announced the hospital's reaction to the request for René's re-admittance loudly and clearly.

'The hospital refuses even to consider the matter. The deceased has been prepared for cremation. He must be cremated forthwith or the police will be informed.'

Yvonne finished her whisky and rose to her feet again, magnificent in defeat. 'Your arm, please, Eric,' she said proudly. I gave her my arm and we went down to the undertaker's car.

From then on everything seemed to move very quickly like a two-reel Buster Keaton. The undertaker had been speaking the truth. We were by then within minutes of losing our place in the queue at Vevey. The hearse shot away from the hospital with Yvonne and me in the second car after it. The secondary roads were often not much more than narrow lanes and the hearse driver in front was a demon. Yvonne became quite animated and exclaimed with delight when we shaved past a farm tractor. She drew another deep breath and then turned to me, her eyes gleaming. 'René's Last Ride,' she cried and made it sound like a John Ford Western.

We reached the crematorium only just in time to prevent another funeral party getting our place. They had to wait. Yvonne didn't care; as our mourners filed into the chapel for the ceremony she seized my arm and took me with her following the coffin on its way to the business end of the crematorium at the back. 'We must say goodbye to René', she said; 'allons.'

When we caught up with the hearse the undertaker and his men were carrying the wreaths through a back door of the chapel and the coffin was being manhandled on to a flimsy metal trolley by three old men in work smocks. The sudden eruption of Yvonne into their territory upset them. Calling 'René' in a loud voice she made as if to throw herself at the coffin, the small end of which was already on the trolley. The old man holding the trolley backed off, the trolley swerved and the wooden lid of the coffin slid off sideways. It had not been screwed down and now one could see why. The fine hardwood box had been only for show; inside it was the plastic coffin that was going into the crematorium furnace. It was of plastic foam, the kind of white moulded material now used for shipping electronic things like video cassette players and personal computers. Unfortunately, the lid of the inner coffin was also unfastened – candidates for cremation must be accompanied by a doctor's identification certificate – and as one of the other old men tried to save the wooden lid from falling he knocked the plastic lid completely off. At the same moment the third old man pulled the trolley out of harm's way and let the end of the coffin fall. Yvonne cried 'René' again and, lo and behold, he stood before us. Well, almost stood.

He was wearing a dark-blue suit, a white poplin shirt and a Chavet tie. His hands were neatly crossed on his breast, his eyes were closed and his lips were set in a little pout of displeasure. I had seen that pout before, when a bottle of wine he had taken some trouble over turned out to be corky and when the colonel had set up a ping-pong table on the lawn just under the Thierens' balcony. But it was inefficiency rather than misfortune and madness that triggered that pout more often. One could, after all, try another bottle of the wine and one could wait with crossed fingers for that fool of a colonel's doctor to tell him that fast ping-pong with teenage sons as opponents was inviting an early coronary; but where flagrant inefficiency was concerned there was nothing to be done but to start firing. In a life of steel he had seen it happen again and again; he had made it happen himself. One ignored middle management and disposed of the real incompetents at the top.

At the Vevey crematorium middle management disposed of us quite quickly and politely. They were used to lunatics and indignation. By the time the canned Bach cantata had been played we were almost back on the undertaker's time schedule. There was no clergyman of any denomination present. René and Yvonne had always been agnostics. The cantata had been played to cover a passage of time and to make it seem as if the ashes of the deceased were already all that remained of him; and, of course, to show a proper respect for his passing. The bankers did not stay for the smoked salmon sandwiches and champagne to follow; once the formalities were over they preferred to leave everything to the lawyer.

When we lived in California it had been the custom for persons of our age to have an annual medical check-up. The custom had been a ritual and so, naturally, there had been jokes about it: the oldest was the one about the man who, having had everything checked – heart, lungs, liver, kidneys, blood and central nervous system – and everything found good, walks out of the doctor's office and dies of a massive coronary while waiting for the elevator. It was no doubt a true story and everyone smiled a little at it, but they still had their check-ups. If anything looked wrong and the patient could afford it he would be shipped off to one of the assembly-line consultancy organizations, like the Mayo Clinic, for a really big definitive check-up. The medical insurance assessors believed in the check-up system. Not to believe in it was like not cleaning one's teeth, or not believing that prevention was better than cure.

In Switzerland, as in the rest of Europe, a patient goes to see a doctor when he has an unfamiliar illness or pain that he cannot treat hmself. What he seeks is diagnosis and either treatment or reassurance. Of course, it helps, and saves time, if he is already known to the doctor, but a copy of last year's check-up results is not the same thing as a medical history.

Joan was used to the American way and when I lived there I acepted it too. Both of us submitted to medical insurance policy examinations in the same week. We were the same age and both in work. Joan was pronounced A1; I emerged as uninsurable. No reason was given other than the bromide about these verdicts being actuarially determined. Joan certainly looked better than I did and, heard through a stethoscope, probably sounded better too.

We were in our early seventies when things began to go wrong. Joan had bought the film rights of a story by H.E. Bates and had asked Peter Hall, the stage director, to collaborate with her on the script. The star was to be James Mason, by then a close neighbour in Switzerland.

The onset of Joan's illness was 'insidious'. I had sometimes encountered the word in medical literature and wondered how such a melodramatic adjective – 'treacherous, crafty, proceeding or progressing secretly or subtly' according to the OED – could have a medical use. I understand better now. The onset of Joan's illness was subtle and altogether secret; the illness did not even have a name.

That spring we went for a spell to Los Angeles and stayed at a small hotel on Wilshire near the Country Club. Inquiries soon revealed that the doctor with the best reputation as a diagnostician had an office in Beverly Hills. He was Billy Wilder's doctor and since Billy was a friend of ours the doctor was helpful in finding time to take Joan's case. There were two weeks of tests, some of which had already been done in London, but no clear diagnosis. The last and most important service this doctor performed for us was to write a letter to our GP in London reporting his findings and suggesting that a neurologist be consulted. The possibility of there being a brain tumour was touched upon.

The Computerized Axial Tomography Scanner was invented in Britain and first used there. Among the many things it made possible was speedy and comprehensive radiological examination of the brain. When we returned to Europe from that Los Angeles spring we did not know that the CT scanner existed. Our GP did, however; he also knew how to gain access to one of these scarce machines and a consultant neurologist who could interpret the machine's findings.

Joan and I went together to hear what the University College Hospital consultant had to say. He was, and is, a plain speaker.

'The good news is that there is no brain tumour.'

The less good news was that there was, nevertheless, plainly discernible brain damage. Causes unknown, as they were unknown in other diseases of this sort; one saw it mostly in the common dementias like Alzheimer's disease, Pick's disease and Creuzfeldt-Jakob. When we know the causes of this kind of atrophy we can look for a cure. In the meantime the answer was care and management.

That was almost fifteen years ago. The care has been professional; the courage has been Joan's. We sold the apartment in Switzerland. Invalid care is more easily managed in one's native language.

It was strange living in England again; at first there was so much catching up to do; and there was such an unpleasant smell in the London air, like that of a cheap air freshener and particularly noticeable around the skirts of the mother of parliaments. The smell was that of decaying cover-up and PR work, of course, and such messes should have been cleared up, but the English had got into the habit of believing that corruption and turpitude in high places only happened abroad; and in the face of all the evidence to the contrary the habit lingered.

Even more deeply ingrained was the British habit of groundless national self-congratulation.

The modern youth cult was first identified as a twentieth-century social novelty by academic anthropologists working in mid-thirties New Deal America. It was quickly recognized, however, that Madison, Ohio, where the first work had been done, was typical not only of middle America, but of most of the large towns and cities of the United States; this teenage thing was an All-American high school student phenomenon and of immediate economic importance. When, twenty years later, the same teenage phenomenon showed up in England it was treated not as a predictable side-effect of Marshall Plan aid flowing into the economy, but hailed as a post-war triumph of the British people's genius for creating new social institutions.

What had happened in Marshall-aided England was what had happened earlier in New Deal America: the in-work non-professional classes had suddenly become prosperous and their adolescent children had found themselves with money to spend. The difference between the two movements had been the music to which they marched. The American kids had had the big band sound and 78 rpm records. The British youth had had rock-and-roll, pop groups and 45 rpm singles. The American kids of that first generation had gone to World War Two. The British lot, liberated by the pill, saw a future of eternal youth. Their swinging sixties became the pelvis-tilting seventies. In the eighties overweight whizkids at the dealing desks of the money and stock markets began to call themselves yuppies. It was reassuring to discover that British trains no longer ran on time; a few boys of the old brigade had evidently retained enough strength to work to rule.

The Detection Club was still very much alive, and I was still, it seemed, a member. I had been elected in 1952 when Dorothy L. Sayers was president, though no longer an active holder of the office. If she had been active I probably would not have been elected or even proposed. I wrote thrillers, not detective novels, and I would certainly not have sworn solemnly 'never to conceal a vital clue from the reader' at my initiation. Come to think of it, I never was initiated; I was proposed and I was accepted, though I cannot now remember who my proposer was. It must have been a member I already knew – either John Dickson Carr, Michael Gilbert or Julian Symons – and one who knew that I was not given to swearing foolish oaths. What I enjoyed about the Detection Club was the friendliness and conviviality of its meetings, qualities not characteristic of most gatherings of writers. Fortunately for me Miss Sayers no longer attended the meetings. I cannot believe that we would have seen eye to eye about anything.

It has always been a pleasure to see Julian Symons again. With him and his wife Kathleen there, almost any occasion becomes a pleasure. I remember in particular a weekend in Berlin. The city still had its odious Wall, and we were there with the help, encouragement and blessing of the British Council to show that British thriller writers cared and that if we could hit upon a magic trumpet note that would bring the Wall down we would happily sound it. Instead we talked to the Berliners and they talked back. I had not expected to enjoy myself. Thanks to Julian, who chaired the meetings, I did. When the Detection Club asked for a short detective story to celebrate his eightieth birthday I was happy to try.

The One Who Did for Blagden Cole is not really a detective story; none of the founder members of the Detection Club would have accepted it as such. It amused Julian though, and I have changed it only very slightly here and there: not to propitiate the shade of Dorothy Sayers, but to indulge my own belief that for a writer of fiction all changes that he makes himself are likely to be for the better.

The One Who Did For Blagden Cole

FELIX Everard Cole, the English painter who signed himself Blag or Blagden Cole, has been dead for over sixty years; yet only now is he beginning to be recognized as one of our century's masters. The catalogue notes of last year's retrospective at the Royal Academy attempted somewhat obscurely to explain the delay.

He was a draughtsman to be compared with Constantin Guys whom Monet admired and whose praises were sung by Baudelaire. As a painter he developed, as did other young Post-Impressionists of the Julian school, in the long shadow cast by Puvis de Chavannes, but he soon became drawn to the Intimism of Vuillard. He even studied for a while with the Synthetiste Paul Sérusier, an influence that may have contributed to the later richness of his palette and the charm of his Bonnard-like interiors. None the less, it was as a portrait painter that he fulfilled himself; and it was, perhaps, his commercial success as a theatrical portraitist that suspended and then postponed judgement on his work as a whole. He died, absurdly and mysteriously, at the height of his powers.

And so on.

Now, God help us, there is to be an official biography.

There is nothing absurd about a shot-gun blast at close range. The note-writer is wrong, too, about the dangers to a painter of commercial success. Those who deal in the reputations of dead artists – art historians, curators, senior auction-house appraisers – are rarely moralists but they are inclined to take themselves and their work seriously. They despise the snap judgements of popular taste. They hate to see art written about and hear it spoken of as if it were a branch of show business or the women's fashion trade. They are intellectual snobs, of course, but they are not fools. In our day there have been few good artists who have been able to avoid the attentions of the press or tried very hard to do so. Publicity has usually brought work. But the young Blagden Cole had sometimes gone too far. He had seemed to court publicity and controversy for their own sakes. Moreover he did so at a time before the 1914–18 war when popular newspapers were building national circulations. Their stock-in-trade was the common touch, but the touch had to be firm and sure of itself. To the fringe editorial staff of Harmsworth's *Daily Mail*, informed jokers like Blag Cole were invaluable. When Blag made fun of Clive Bell and the Contemporary Art Society, readers could understand the jokes. When Bloomsbury hit back by describing Blag Cole's talent as 'the fine commercial knack of making rich grocers look interesting' the *Mail* printed that too. Some of its keenest readers were grocers. All Blag achieved was notoriety.

It was about then that he took to signing his work 'Blag'. He had never liked his given names. His mother had been a music teacher and the Felix had been her salute to the memory of Mendelssohn, one of her favourite composers. Blagden was her family name and Blagden Cole looked and sounded more interesting than Felix Cole. The abbreviation to Blag developed after the death of his sister Cécile, named after the other favourite composer Chaminade. Blag liked the abbreviation pronounced with a long *a*, as in the French word *blague* meaning a bad joke or trick. He made other enemies in those early years, and not just in Bloomsbury. Appointed as War Artist to the British expeditionary force on the Salonika front, he was the direct cause of a diplomatic incident.

The Army of the Orient based on Salonika was a multi-national force. Besides the two British divisions, mostly survivors of the Gallipoli campaign, there were French, Serbian, Italian and Greek troops. The army commander was General Sarrail, an affable Frenchman with a soldierly bearing and a taste for political intrigue. He lived in a small palace in some state with his mistress, a Russian princess of great beauty with an astonishing taste in hats. The troops lived in tented camps among the malaria swamps of the Vardar valley with sand-fly fever and dysentery for company. A large Bulgarian army was dug in on the heights above and, although most of the Allied casualties were caused by disease, Bulgarian sniper fire added substantially to the account. Morale was low; the troops thought of themselves as forgotten; and not without reason.

The nearest the General ever went to a forward area was the Cercle Militaire, a French officers' club near their corps HQ. It was at this club that Blag heard from a correspondent of the Havas news agency about a review of troops planned for the Fourteenth of July. It was expected that, despite advice from Paris that the lady was spying for King Ferdinand of Bulgaria, the General's noble mistress would be beside him on the reviewing stand. Photographers would be forbidden but who would notice a sketch artist in British uniform sitting on the edge of the parade ground?

No one did, and the pen-and-ink drawing Blag made from his sketch was smuggled to the Havas office in Paris via the Italian diplomatic bag. The magazine *L'Illustration* gave it a full page. They dared to publish it partly because it was strongly reminiscent of Guys at his best, partly because Havas had declared (truthfully) that none of the Allied censors in Salonika had objected to the work and partly because it was felt that Clemenceau the new Prime Minister would not object to British criticism of a French general whom he was known to despise.

The drawing shows Sarrail taking the salute at a march past of high-stepping Senegalese infantry. He is standing, hand at kepi, in an open horse-drawn carriage. Hovering over him, however, are the plumes of an enormous hat, that of his princess. She is standing slightly behind him in all her statuesque glory, protecting him from the sun with her parasol. The drawing has a caption in English: 'General Sarrail reviews his presidential guard.' It is signed 'Blag d'après Guys'.

Unfortunately, Clemenceau did object, strongly. The British prime minister had chosen that moment to write to him personally about Salonika. Not only did he question Sarrail's fitness for command (as everyone else did) but he had also had the impertinence to suggest that the British and French colonial components of the Army of the Orient would be better employed on the Western front in place of the French divisions there which had recently mutinied. Coming on top of the Blag drawing, with its insulting use of the phrase 'presidential guard', the whole affair looked like a planned provocation and an attempt to humiliate France. French intelligence agreed and blamed the British secret service in Athens. Who but the British could employ their official war artist in Greece to discredit their French ally?

Blag was threatened with a court martial, but lied his way out of it. His story was that he had been asked to do the drawing by the French Cercle Militaire to hang with other pictures on the wall of their bar room, and since he was an honorary member of the Cercle he had been glad to do it. He had not been paid for the drawing. Its removal to France and reproduction in *L'Illustration* had nothing to do with him. The British force commander, himself an occasional guest at the Cercle, confirmed the findings of a Court of Inquiry in Blag's favour. He had escaped the military danger, but the offence given had been almost wholly political and the politicians were not disposed to let the prank go unpunished. His accreditation as an official War Artist was withdrawn and he was sent home.

There Sir Alfred Harmsworth had been translated into Lord Northcliffe and his *Daily Mail* had become a power in the land. Blag's old editorial acquaintances were not really pleased to see him, even when he told them the truth about the Sarrail affair. The word from on high was that he should be regarded as Bolshie, a new term then used to describe those likely to become mutinous. Besides, Sarrail had already been replaced by General Franchet d'Espèrey who didn't live in a palace with a Russian mistress. Blag was advised to watch his step and do something ostentatiously patriotic, like a royal portrait. No, of course he couldn't get a commission to paint royalty just at the moment. The black mark would have to fade. Perhaps he should volunteer to do war work of some sort, for the Society of Friends, maybe, or the Red Cross.

He seemed struck with the idea and asked for an introduction to a committee member of the Red Cross. They gave him one. The result, however, was not at all what they had expected. When Blag had been sent home he had taken all his sketchbooks with him. Nobody had tried to stop him taking them, not even the censors at base. So now he took the sketchbooks to the Red Cross. He had an offer to make and a proposal. If the Red Cross committee would choose one hundred sketches from the hundreds in the books he, Blag, would make a hundred finished pictures of them. Most would be on double demy board, some line-and-wash, some gouache, some pastel. With the hundred pictures the Red Cross could mount an international fund-raising exhibition.

That it was such an extraordinary success was only partly due to Blag and his work. Timing and the fortunes of war were on his side, for it was in the late summer of 1918 that the forgotten Army of the Orient came into its own. The faces of the men Blag had sketched in 1917 were the faces of those who next year fought their way through the Balkans to the first Central Powers surrender of the war. There were the faces of Frenchmen and Englishmen, of Chasseurs alpins and South Wales Borderers, of the Scottish Brigade and Moroccan Cavalrymen, of pilots of the 47 Squadron RAF who won the Kosturino Pass and Spahis watering their horses in the Struma river. The exhibition catalogue became a collector's item and sold well at charity auctions. Blag's name became very well known. An eccentric British peer tried to sue him for unlawfully disposing of Crown copyrights. The French gave him a Légion d'Honneur. In London he was offered accreditation as an Official Artist to the Paris Peace Conference. He refused on the grounds that the spectacle of Allied politicians drawing battle maps for the next war was a job for a caricaturist. He was going back to painting portraits.

And he did. By the twenties he was, undeniably, the most fashionable portrait painter. He also dabbled in the theatre. He designed a ballet for Diaghilev and collaborated with Komisarjevsky in the design of a production of *Peer Gynt*. He experimented with lithography. It is possible that he did too much and that some of his work then did not show him at his best. Most of it did, though, and in the last year of his life he was certainly at his best. He did indeed die 'at the height of his powers'. It has been only the manner and mystery of his death that have obscured the fact. But the work has survived that long expert scrutiny and his reputation is at last secure. His messy death is no longer seen as an admission of artistic failure comparable with that of Benjamin Haydon. It is now seen as an act of voluntary euthanasia committed to terminate a life of mental suffering which had become intolerable.

Seen by the pundits that is. But not by the biographer. Now, all the old lies and the old agonies are to be dredged up and picked over again by this less fastidious seeker after truth. I understand that he writes thrillers under another name; he is high minded, a moralizer. He says that, as the only surviving witness and as the subject of the last portrait Blag painted, I have a moral duty to unburden myself.

He does not say 'spill the beans'; but that is what he means. I have been expecting something like this to happen ever since the picture with that tell-tale date on it turned up at Christie's last year and fetched that huge price. I had been hoping, in the way the old do, that I would be dead before someone started asking questions and that my executors would be left to cope. But the biographer invites me to 'unburden myself'. Some years ago a publisher asked me to write a piece about Blag's last days and I refused easily. I am a truth-teller of sorts but the theatre is my medium. Still, there is a need in the old to unburden which can become as urgent as the need to confess guilt.

As a boy I knew Blag as a friend of the family. After my father died Blag became for a few weeks a benefactor.

My parents were actors, Harry and Kitty Blagden, and they spent most of their working lives on tour or in provincial rep. My brother and I lived with Grandma Blagden in Clapham. It was there, when our parents were at home resting, that we heard all the gossip. In the autumn of 1919, after the Treaty of Versailles was signed, they were in Birmingham doing a season of rep. One of the plays was Ibsen's *Ghosts*, still a very daring play then. My mother played Regina and my father Pastor Manders. The local bishop preached against it. It was quite a hit. The theatre was next door to a municipal art gallery and the curator there was stage-struck. It was he who made the connection between Blagden Cole and the production of *Ghosts* with my parents in it. Part of the gallery was devoted at that moment to an exhibition of modern portraits and among them was a portrait of his mother by Cole. The picture was signed but not dated. What only the curator knew was that on the back of the canvas were scrawled the words, 'Portrait of Mrs Alving by her son Oswald'. That was dated 1912.

That was the year *Ghosts* had its first public performance in a London theatre and audiences had been deeply shocked. The

155

subject of hereditary disease had until then been strictly taboo. Ibsen used it as a symbol for moral corruption, but the disease he had had in mind was generally assumed to be congenital syphilis. An artist who signed a portrait of his mother as Mrs Alving's doomed son Oswald was making a harsh statement. My father already knew Blag well. They had met in the dog days of 1917 at the base hospital in Salonika, my father a convalescent subaltern in the Welsh Fusiliers. He had become friendly enough with Blag and one of the doctors there to know that Blag believed himself the potential victim of a disease that 'ran in the family'.

In Birmingham my parents tried to persuade the rep management to forget the curator's amusing little discovery, but in vain. Blag was news and they could use the publicity. A London paper picked up the story from the local rag and asked Blag to comment. He denied all knowledge of the *Ghosts* inscription on the portrait and wasn't too sure that he remembered the portrait itself. He would ask his mother what had happened to it. But he was delighted to hear that his old army pal Harry Blagden had survived the war. No, no relation but the same family name. A fine actor, Harry. He himself meant to go up and see the play.

He went the following week. It wasn't *Ghosts* he saw, but the Frederick Lonsdale comedy that alternated with it. For that my father was thankful. He had not believed Blag's denial of the *Ghosts* inscription. He knew that for Blag 1912 had been a bad year in more ways than one. He had heard Blag telling a friendly doctor all about it in the Salonika hospital. During the year ending in the spring of 1912 Blag's sister Cécile had died in a mental home; and Blag had witnessed the process of her dying. The thought of Blag sitting in the stalls watching the final scene of *Ghosts*, with Oswald centre stage, deserted by Regina and watched only by his mother, crying out for the sun as he sinks into imbecility, would have been unbearable.

My mother liked Blag from the first. They talked about the war, of course, and about amoebic dysentery and malaria being better for an actor than losing an arm or a leg. But Blag knew why your father wasn't playing leads. He knew that Harry's illness was worse than serious. He said that us Blagdens ought not to trust army medical boards. He said that the only medicine they understood was a disability pension table. He was right too. He knew all about the Blagden families and which lot came from where. His came from Lancashire. Your father's came from Yorkshire via London, as you know.'

'But Blagden was his mother's family.'

'His father had no family to speak of. Anyway he was no good. When Blag was only six Mr Cole ran off to America without a word and died there. Old Mrs Cole made a living of sorts teaching music but it was the Blagden drapery business that paid most of the bills. That's how Blag started as an artist you know. He went to a Manchester art school to learn textile design.'

'Was his father an artist, the one who ran away?'

'Not him. He was a piano tuner by trade. I think he sold insurance too, as a sideline. Blag doesn't like talking about him.'

That was just after my own father died in 1922. It was the undiagnosed diabetes that killed him, not the ailments they had been treating him for. Not that it would have made any difference. Insulin was discovered just too late to help him. It was a terrible year but it became a year of decision. Granny couldn't keep house for all of us with no money coming in. Mother had marvellous legs and could move beautifully on a big stage. She had been asked to go into panto before but couldn't because of my father. Now she accepted.

Her first principal boy was Prince Charming in the Moss Empire production of *Cinderella* at the Grand, Leeds. And that was when we discovered what a good friend Blag could be. The show was rehearsed in London but dress-rehearsed in Leeds. Blag talked to the London management publicity people and arranged to attend the Leeds lighting and dress rehearsals. There he did croquis and drawings of all the principal actors. They were the sorts of drawings and sketches that Lautrec might have done – simple, sad and wonderfully elegant. The drawing of Kitty Blagden as Prince Charming was particularly fine. It was published with a page to itself in the *Bystander*, a London magazine that reported the doings of the smart set and the bright young things. Her agent always said that it was his astute use of the Prince Charming drawing that promoted her from the provinces to the West End stage. Agent or no agent, she began to get flattering work in musical comedy and then in a series of Charlot revues.

157

Blag lived in the country just outside London and for a year or two we saw quite a lot of him. It was my younger brother who had the temerity to ask one evening, after Blag had taken my mother to lunch at the Savoy, if they were going one day to get married.

If I had dared to ask such a question I would have been damned for my impudence. My brother was only told not to be silly and to go and do his homework. My grandmother had gone to her Thursday whist drive. We were sitting at the kitchen table where I had supper and my mother had tea and a sandwich before leaving for the theatre. When my brother had gone she gave me a look.

'Did you put him up to that, Charlie? No? Then what's he been reading? *Peg's Paper*?'

'He asked me, I didn't know what to say. I still don't.'

'Well, I suppose I'd better tell you. The answer is no. Blag would like to get married but not to his old friend's widow even if she was willing. What he needs is a young wife who'll give him a good time. He could have that, but that's not what he wants. What he wants is a young wife who'll give him children. And that he can't have – mustn't have.'

'Sins of the fathers? Ghosts?'

'Not the sins that you mean. There are other things beside VD that people can inherit. Things that run in a family for generations, like red hair or blue blood. Only some of them are killers. The one waiting for Blag is called Huntington's chorea and I'd rather not talk about it at table.'

'You said that it's waiting for him. Does he know?'

'He can't know for certain. It got his father when he was in his forties. The father's mother died of it while he was still an infant in arms. Blag's sister was just thirty. He's lasted the longest. If it was only syphilis he could have a blood test and know. But there's no test for Huntington's and he could still be a carrier. There's no need to tell your brother all this, of course. Heaven knows what fairy tales he'd invent. Your father told me most of it.' She glanced at her watch. 'Which reminds me. About a year ago Blag sent your father the synopsis of an idea for a play. If it survived the nursing home tidy-up he'd like it back. But I'm not going to go through your father's papers. You're the man of the house now. You

158

find it. It'll be in one of the big suitcases. I must be off, I'm late already.'

I found it eventually, between his army papers and a war diary. It was written on two pieces of Elm Park Farm letter paper. The provisional title of Blag's play was *A Respectable Woman's Guide to Murder* and it was based on the life of Madeleine Smith. She was tried in 1857 for poisoning her lover, escaped the gallows by looking invincibly respectable and lived happily ever after, with a succession of legal husbands, until well into the nineteen twenties. What caught my eye first, however, was the folded paper to which the synopsis had been pinned. When unpinned and unfolded this turned out to be an art gallery reproduction of Toulouse-Lautrec's famous poster portrait of the cabaret singer Aristide Bruant. In the margin there was a scribbled note in Blag's writing.

'You asked why I never did self-portraits. Here's one reason. I never saw Bruant or heard him sing and I never wore a big black cape with a red scarf like this. Far too actory. But I must admit to finding that somewhat Napoleonic profile an astonishing likeness. More so as I grow older.'

And it was indeed an astonishing likeness. No doubt the cape was a prop designed to conceal short legs and a pot belly. Blag didn't need it. He was tall and lanky. The Bruant profile, though, was just right. I went back to the play synopsis. On a space at the foot of the second page my father had pencilled a note.

'Madeleine Smith is an interesting subject and there have been several attempts to dramatize her. At the moment, I hear, a Hollywood producer wants to make a film about her. She objects. She now lives in America, is over ninety, still highly respectable and will have the law on anyone who says different. Better wait a bit. The theme will keep.'

I put the synopsis in an envelope, addressed it to Blag at Elm Park Farm, near Pinner, Middlesex and wondered if I could find some inexpensive way of delivering it in person instead of sending it by post. I had always been curious about Elm Park Farm. My mother had spent weekends there and had been very enthusiastic. 'It's neither a park nor a farm,' she had explained once; 'but it used to be both. Now, it just shows you what a good architect can do with a walled garden, a Victorian stable yard

159

and a fire-gutted Regency house.' For guests it was 'delici-
ously comfortable', though she didn't much care for old Mrs
Cole, the 'eternal music teacher'. However, Aunt Alice, her
sister, wasn't a bad sort. 'Tweedy. Plays golf.'

Luckily, I remembered something else my mother had said.
'It's easy to get to. You take the Metropolitan line to Pinner
and Blag has a hire car waiting at the station to pick you up. Or
you can go to Rickmansworth and get a country bus.' I posted
the synopsis with the Lautrec repro to Blag and consoled
myself with the diary.

It wasn't really about the war; it was about the efforts of a
professional actor with a 'hostilities-only' commission in the
Fusiliers to run an army divisional concert party in northern
Greece. This was between courses of treatment at a military
field hospital. There were long lists of names taken at audi-
tions with comments on the participants – mostly *nbg*. There
were the occasional discoveries – 'Cpl Hughes R. fair baritone,
better pianist, can sight-read and transpose.' The times he
spent in hospital seemed, on the whole, more enjoyable. The
doctors had a mess tent to themselves which he was allowed to
use; an actor who can tell funny stories well is always good
company. It was there that he got to know Blag who had done
a lot of sketching in the hospital. Blag was popular in the mess
because he brought the high command gossip he picked up
from the Italians and the French. He also liked talking medical
'shop'. The doctors didn't mind this because, for a layman, he
was well informed, particularly about diseases of the central
nervous system. On the subject of child-birth, however, he
could make a fool of himself. My father recorded a boozy
Burns night dialogue between Blag and the Scottish senior
surgeon.

Blag: Jock, I tell you this with my hand on my heart. I was
   born two months premature and I weighed nine pounds.
Surgeon: You can put your hand where you like, Blag my boy,
   but you canna have it both ways. Nine pounds you may
   have been, but if so you weren't premature. Or if you were
   premature you didna weigh nine pounds. Who told you this
   fairy tale? A midwife? Ah, those old biddies will say anything if they think you want to hear it.

Blag's reply was to get up from the dinner table and leave the
mess without another word. My father noted that this was the
only time he saw Blag behave less than well. As it was Burns
night none of the Scots there took any notice. On Burns night
anyone was likely to behave badly. 'Poor Blag,' had been my
father's comment; 'he must have known the date of his parents'
wedding day.'

Why poor? In the end I asked my mother. She sighed. 'Really
Charlie, I should have thought it was obvious. When there's
something that runs in the family, even little things, everyone
wants to know what he or she was like as a baby. Even in normal
families there's a lot of lies and careful talk about such things. If
he was born a nine-pound baby boy, the doctor says, he wasn't
premature. So, mother Cole was nine months pregnant with
him. She had been pregnant on her wedding day. These things
happen all the time. It was a wicked world, Charlie, even in
good Queen Victoria's day, God rest her soul. What are you
grinning at? It's not funny. Young Emma Blagden, the sprightly
little music teacher, had a romp before she was supposed to
with person or persons unknown.'

'The piano tuner?'

'Who doubled as an insurance agent? The Huntington's
carrier? Poor Blag must have hoped that it was someone else.
Especially after the death of his sister.'

'He could have asked his mother. I mean, she'd have to tell
him the truth, wouldn't she?'

My mother gave me an extra long look. 'Tell you what,
Charlie,' she said; 'if you're ever invited to Elm Park Farm and
you meet old Mrs Cole, you can ask her that question yourself.'

My young brother James got to the Farm first. Nineteen
twenty-six was a bad year for our family. Granny Blagden,
whose house we had always lived in, had to go into a nursing
home for a minor operation. It went wrong and she died there.
Mother was in one show and rehearsing for another. Things had
to be done like paying the nursing home in order to get the
death certificate. Blag came to the rescue. He dealt with
the nursing home then took me to the undertakers who had the
body in their mortuary. With them he was equally firm. Just
the motor hearse and one car for mourners. A plain oak coffin is
what your grandmother would have wanted, eh Charles? and

not those fancy bronze handles, please, the ordinary brass ones. He gave the name of his own solicitor in Covent Garden as the one who would be probating the Will. He did not mention that she had drawn it up herself on a form bought at the local stationers.

We buried Granny in the morning three days later. When we got back to the house we were joined by Blag's lawyer who said that Granny had read the Will form instructions carefully and followed them. The house was the major part of her estate and she had left it to Mother. For her there were two immediate problems. The first was that of finding a live-in cook-housekeeper to replace Granny. The second, to my surprise, was that of my matric. I was due to sit for it in two weeks' time. If I didn't sit for it, my mother declared, and if I didn't pass with honours, I couldn't go to college. She had promised my father that I would do both. She knew of an out-of-work dresser who could be trusted to keep house for a week or two if one strictly rationed the gin. Blag said that, if I were to be kept busy preparing for an exam and keeping an eye on the gin, my brother might like to spend some time at the Farm. As it was getting near the end of term he was sure the school would agree. All James wanted to know was whether there was a piano at the Farm. On being told sharply by my mother that Mrs Cole had two pianos and that if he behaved himself she might let him try the Broadwood grand James gave Blag a beatific smile. At thirteen my brother was already a practised charmer.

Of course, we all knew by then that he had a musical talent. He wasn't a prodigy but he was clearly exceptional. Mother knew people at the Guildhall School and the professor who had heard James play had assured her that there would be a scholarship for him a bit later on. Obviously, a few weeks in the country playing on a good piano before an audience as experienced and sympathetic as Mrs Cole (herself a Blagden) would be weeks well spent.

According to James it was time wasted and a setback to his career as a musician. The stables, studios and gardens were all right, spiffing indeed, but Mrs Cole, Auntie Alice and their house were all *ghastly*. 'Don't misunderstand me, Charlie, it's a very *pretty* place. There's a small river that runs through it with willow trees along the bank and a path to the village. The real farm, the old eighty-one-acre one, is on the other side of the river. It belongs to a real farmer now. The real old house was commandeered in the war as a convalescent home for the shell-shock cases. Jack Hunter says that it was the shell-shock cases who set fire to it on Armistice night.'

'Who is Jack Hunter?'

'He was one of the shell-shock patients. He and his wife Annette run the whole place for Blag. Annette does the cooking. She's Belgian.'

'What's the cooking like?'

'Oh, I was at Mrs Cole's house. Auntie Alice does the cooking there. They have a girl in from the village to do the cleaning and the beds. The Lancashire hotpot was all right.'

'But not the piano?'

'The piano was all right. It was her. The moment I got there she said she was going to give me lessons. And she'd even bought me a party piece to learn.'

'Chopin. Something flashy.'

'She gave me a choice. One of Mendelssohn's *Songs without Words* – she called it "The Bees' Wedding" – or else "Kitten on the Keys" by Zez Confrey. Auntie Alice had a gramophone record of that. She called it ragtime.'

'Which did you choose?'

'"Kitten". It's not really difficult but it does need what Professor Brant calls dexterity. Besides, Mrs C. wanted me to choose the other one. She's weird. She gives a concert recital every evening at six. She always has the lid of the piano right up and all the windows open. It's always when Blag's walking along the river path to the village pub for a drink. She plays Chaminade's "Autumn" at him full blast. She says it's to remind him of Cécile. Who's Cécile? He never takes any notice unless he has someone with him, like Jennifer or Rowe. Then he just waves. Jack Hunter shoots the rabbits because they're pests. If I were Blag I'd ask him to shoot her. You know, she even marked the fingering for me on the music.'

I asked mother who Rowe and Jennifer were. My brother had banished Elm Park Farm to an outer limbo. My mother made sense.

'Didn't I tell you? One side of the old stables has been

163

converted into two biggish studios with living quarters attached. Tom McGowan has one. He's an engraver and an old friend of Blag's. Jennifer, his daughter, keeps house for him and does a little book illustrating. Nice girl. Lost the boy she was going to marry on the Somme. Ruskin Rowe has the other studio. He's a commercial photographer. Things not people. Very clever I'm told. It's a bit like a Mayfair mews down there. Without Blag it could get artsy crafty.'

'Where is his studio then?'

'Behind the garden wall. As far away from his mother and his Aunt Alice as he can reasonably be. You'll see. He's bound to ask you down. He said he'd like to draw you. He sees your father in you. So do I, come to that. You've got to go to college.'

There was no help for it; I had to work harder. Just over a year later I jumped through the necessary hoops, passed the right exams and acted my way past an interview board. In September, when I was eighteen, I could go to college and read law at the taxpayers' expense. My mother was very pleased. Since she was in the new Noël Coward revue she was also disposed to be generous. She bought me some new shirts and underwear and decided that I had grown enough to wear one of my father's Savile Row suits. She also said that when my last term at school ended I should have a holiday. The invitation from Blag came two days later. It was in the form of a job offer; that of temporary assistant gardener. The pay offered was two pounds a week plus bed, full board and beer money.

'But two pounds is a lot,' I protested. 'I'm no gardener.'

'He knows that, silly. It's just a way of giving pocket money. Besides, think of the food. Annette runs her kitchen like a French bistro. All you'll have to do for yourself is make your bed.'

I didn't know what a bistro was, but I soon found that I was going to have a better time at Elm Park Farm than my brother. I had one of the guest-rooms built over the old coach house with a view of the river, and its own bathroom next door. It was entered from a balcony that ran the length of the stable yard from the walled garden to 'The Lodge', the small house with the clock tower in which the Hunters lived. The balcony was reached by an iron spiral staircase. Blag himself showed me the way.

'This place is run like a boarding-house,' he explained, 'with Annette as the landlady. The studios, mine included, all have their own kitchens but artists and craftsmen don't always feel like cooking. Some of us aren't very good cooks anyway. Sometimes we prefer to eat in dear Annette's kitchen which is conveniently next door to the Lodge where you met Jack just now. Lunch is at one o'clock, dinner at eight. Annette doesn't do breakfasts though, just tea and toast. What do you drink now, Charlie? Wine? Beer?'

'I had a glass of sherry last Christmas.'

'I ask because I'm in the habit of walking along to the village pub for a drink before dinner. I dare say your brother told you. I'm always glad of company. You're allowed to drink in pubs, aren't you? You're eighteen.'

'Almost.'

'It's five now. By the time you've unpacked and found a book to read it'll be sixish. I'll give you a shout.'

The path along the river bank was cool and pleasant in the shade of the willows, but as we came abreast of the monkey puzzle on Mrs Cole's lawn the shade thinned and we had the evening sun directly in our eyes. At the same moment the sound of the piano, of which I had been dimly aware, suddenly became louder. It was the Chaminade all right. I knew because James had picked out the melody on our piano at home the night before. He hadn't wanted me to be caught out if challenged.

Blag wasn't challenging anyone just then, not even his mother. Out of the corner of my eye I saw him raise his arm in acknowledgement of the music as we walked on.

'I dare say your brother told you what to expect,' he said.

'Yes, but I thought the music might have changed. That's not the only piece that Chaminade wrote.'

'Oh, the music changes from time to time. We had Mendelssohn last week. But it's the same old tune really, if you see what I mean, Charlie. By the way she rechristened your brother Zez. After the composer of "Kitten on the Keys". Did he tell you?'

'No. He's rather touchy about his music. He's going steady with Schumann at the moment.'

At the end of the river path there was an iron footbridge

165

across to the farm side of the river. There we joined the cart track that the farmer used to get his milk churns down to the road. Two hundred yards or so further on another footbridge took us back across the river into the rose garden behind The Angler's Rest. There were people sitting at tables on the lawn by the river.

'The flies get in your drink out here,' Blag said and led the way inside.

It wasn't a pub but a gentrified village inn with a courtyard in front and cars with chauffeurs waiting. The owners of the cars were standing in the saloon bar drinking pink gin and whisky on their way home from the day's work. Blag nodded to one or two of them as he led the way through to a room labelled 'BAR PARLOUR'. Here there were tables and chairs and, on the walls, hunting prints and stuffed fish in glass cases. A pretty woman with a nice smile came in to serve us. Her name was Dolly and I was introduced as a kind of nephew.

Dolly beamed. 'Are you Kitty Blagden's boy? There was a lovely picture of her in *Play Pictorial* last month. What'll you drink?'

'How about the draught cider?' said Blag.

'The stuff we've got will give him collywobbles. He'd be safer with a nice long Pimm's. We've got fresh borage. Oh, I was forgetting.' She pulled a letter out of her apron pocket. 'This came for you today by post care of us. Dad said you'd asked him if he minded.' She handed him the letter. 'Gin and tonic for you?'

'Thanks, Dolly.' He looked at the letter. 'Sorry, Charlie. I'd better see what this is.'

I watched him open it. The address on the envelope was typed. I was puzzled. In those days typewritten letters were not as common as they are now. Even business letters were sometimes written by hand. Love letters always were. But why would the master of Elm Park Farm want to use The Angler's Rest as an accommodation address?

When Dolly brought the drinks Blag had his pocket diary open beside the letter. 'I've got a man from Manchester coming down to see me weekend after next,' he said. 'I can't do with him at the Farm. Could you put him up here for a couple of nights? Mr D. J. Bristow. He's a lawyer, quite respectable.'

As we walked back we met Jack Hunter with a shot-gun under his arm. He had been a troop sergeant in the field artillery and in the breeches and leggings which were his weekday work clothes he was still a soldierly figure. He said he was going to shoot rabbits in the farmer's lower field.

'Does he know?' asked Blag.

'He won't argue. If that cowhand of his can't be bothered to keep the rabbits down he'll be getting no more fresh vegetables from us. It's our cold frames those little bunnies like to get into. Talking of which, Mr Blag, your Auntie Alice has been practising her mashie shots again. Broke two panes in the tomato house this evening.'

'I thought you put up some netting for her.'

'She says that's for tee shots, not short approaches. Better watch out as you go by.' He nodded to me and went on his way.

I had no trouble identifying Auntie Alice. She was a white-haired, stubby little woman wearing a pleated tweed skirt, a canary yellow jumper and low-heeled brown brogue shoes. She was now practising chip shots from the edge of the lawn. Sitting at a rustic table by the monkey puzzle tree, and unmistakably mistress of all she surveyed, was Mrs Cole. Her right hand rested on the tasselled handle of a pink parasol which, as we approached, she raised above her head and brandished slightly as if she were hailing a taxi. It would have been difficult for us to have ignored her.

'Better get it over with,' Blag said.

'So this is Zez's big brother Charles,' she said as we approached her. 'Welcome to Elm Park Farm, Charles Blagden.'

'Thank you, Mrs Cole.'

'I never met your father but your mother says you're like him, just as handsome. Are you musical like your brother?'

'Not in the least, Mrs Cole.'

'Modest as well as handsome. You must come to supper with me, young man.'

'That's enough, Em,' said her sister firmly, 'you're making him blush.'

Lancashire still came through clearly in the way Aunt Alice spoke. Mrs Cole had sounded like a drama school elocutionist. I was relieved when Blag took charge again and moved us on.

Mrs Cole's affectations on top of the Pimm's and an otherwise empty stomach had given me an uncontrollable desire to belch. Luckily we were out of earshot before I had to give way. Blag was sympathetic. 'You must be hungry,' he said. 'Annette will soon take care of that.'

Leek and potato soup followed by a chicken casserole with braised endives took care of it very well; and the fact that I can still remember after all these years exactly what was cooked should speak for the quality of Annette's cooking. She was inventive but her dishes were mostly of the pot-au-feu kind, simple but tasty, soups and stews. Since she cooked for so many this was understandable. Her 'kitchen' was two stables knocked into one big room and it had four small tables in it. These could be placed together and she could seat ten if necessary. Usually there were no more than six or seven including her and her husband Jack. They had no children. The real kitchen, where the cooking was done, was in The Lodge next door; an arched doorway connected the two. A sideboard with spirit lamps and hotplates kept the food warm. Everyone, including guests, helped themselves.

I was the only guest that evening but all the residents were there. Tom McGowan, the engraver, and his daughter Jennifer sat at the next table; Rowe, the photographer, was by himself and the Hunters were at the end.

Over the years the portraits Blag did of Jenny have made her beauty as familiar a measure of that quality as Manet's *Olympia* or a Rembrandt portrait of Saskia. At the time, I regret to say, all I saw was a pretty woman with a nice smile and a talent for illustrating children's books.

'What are you going to do with yourself down here?' she asked. 'In Clapham you could have gone to the pictures twice a day.'

'I was hoping he was going to help me plant out the September lettuce,' Jack said loudly. 'Right, sir?'

'It was discussed,' Blag admitted.

'I thought that I was to be allowed to help with the lettuce,' said Rowe and sounded as if he really meant it.

'When I reminded you, Mr Rowe, you said you had a bad back.'

'I'm going to be busy with a sitter for the next two days,' Blag said. 'I'm sure Charlie won't mind giving you a hand, Jack.'

168

'Of course,' I said. Everyone smiled. The formalities were over. A temporary assistant gardener had been engaged. Supplies of September lettuce could now be relied upon.

'You're trapped,' said Jenny; 'mornings from nine to twelve. We can go to the pictures in the afternoon, though, if you like. I can drive us into Rickmansworth.'

'What's on there?' her father asked.

'*Scaramouche* with Ramon Novarro.'

'Face like a rue Blanche pimp,' he said and then turned sideways on his chair to look directly at me. He had a fierce bristly moustache and very sad blue eyes. 'I saw a Henry Blagden on the stage just before the war. He played March-banks in Shaw's *Candida*. Was that your father?'

'Yes, sir. Did you enjoy the play?'

'The play, no. Tiresome, I thought. Your father seemed to make sense of it. Curious.'

'He told me that he played the long speeches as if he were trying to correct a stammer. It took the literary curse off them.'

He grinned. 'There speaks the actor.' He turned back to his plate.

'Charlie's going to be a lawyer, Tom,' Blag said; 'his mother thinks he ought to have a trade.'

They all laughed a little, as if in disbelief. There was both wine and water on the table. I took a little of each. When I got up to my room that night there was an envelope on the dressing table. In it there was a note with two pound notes folded inside it. The note read: 'Congratulations on a skilful performance before a difficult audience. I'll bet you made up that bit about taking the curse off Candida – B.'

Several days went by before I saw Blag again. His sitter was a distinguished actor-manager who lived in Henley and drove over every day in a beautiful Rolls-Royce coupé de ville, the kind of car in which only the chauffeur and front-seat passenger get rained on. Annette sent lunches of smoked salmon sandwiches and chilled Chablis across to the studio. Blag was doing preliminary sketches. The process could go on for days. In the mornings I worked with Jack Hunter, mostly in the greenhouses. These were on the far side of Mrs Cole's house by the vegetable garden where Jack's battle with the farmer's rabbits was fought out. They even got under the wire into the

169

strawberry patch. Jack had to have his shot-gun handy. There was a broom cupboard just inside the back door of the house where Auntie Alice cleaned her golf clubs, so he kept the gun there. The boxes of cartridges he kept in a bag hanging behind the door.

The mornings weren't all gardening. Blag had given the Hunters a four-seater Morris-Cowley in which they used to go shopping for the things that couldn't be delivered, like blocks of ice and boxes of kippers from a fishmonger in Pinner, and wine that had to be fetched from a warehouse near Watford. Jack taught me how to lift cases of wine, as he had taught me how to use a heavy shovel, without doing myself a mischief. The afternoons were restful. I read Aldous Huxley's *Chrome Yellow* and browsed through a stack of old *London Mercury*s. To sustain my impersonation of a law student I had brought a copy of Maitland's *Constitutional History* found secondhand at Foyle's, and became quite fascinated by it. And, of course, I went to the pictures with Jenny. She would have gone every day if there had been enough changes of programme within reasonable driving distance. We went in Blag's car, the old Crossley tourer that Auntie Alice also drove when she went to her golf club. Jenny was a good driver, but the moment we got inside a cinema she became an emotional mess. At least I thought so. She sympathized with the wrong characters. When we saw *Scaramouche*, for instance, she mooned over Lewis Stone who played the wicked marquis, wept for the wooden prettiness of Alice Terry as the heroine and thought nothing at all of Ramon Novarro as the lead. When she had dried her eyes and we were back outside again she seemed quite sensible. I found it disconcerting.

The threatened invitation to supper from Mrs Cole was conveyed by Jack. I was given a choice, Friday or Saturday, so I asked his advice. 'I'd make it Saturday,' he said; 'on Friday it's only high tea with fish cakes and you get the new curate as well. On Saturday it's always a pie from Fortnum's.'

At first it wasn't as bad as I feared. Of course, the recital seemed endless. Raff's 'Cavatina' was added to the usual programme for that week. With the Chaminade finale Auntie Alice poured us both another glass of sherry and brought forward her sister's whisky and soda. Grand piano lids are heavier than they look, but Mrs Cole closed hers with surprising ease. Then, picking up her drink, she sat down with a smile facing me.

'Such a nice cosy woman your mother,' she said; 'has she ever thought of marrying again do you think?'

I was speechless but Auntie Alice filled in for me.

'That's enough, Em,' she said sharply. 'We'll have none of that. You promised.'

It gave me time to become pompous. 'My mother is a highly successful actress,' I said; 'and a highly respected one. She enjoys her work. She has no intention of marrying again. She has told me so.'

'How lucky you are to be trusted with her secrets.'

'No more now, Em. It's time for supper.'

The pie was all right, but I had no appetite.

The following Saturday Mr Bristow arrived. Blag sent Jack with the Morris into Pinner to meet him at the station and take him to The Angler's Rest. Annette and I were having tea when Jack returned. The errand had puzzled him. This Bristow had turned out to be a well-spoken north-country officer type. Why did he have to stay at the pub? There was a spare guest bedroom that he could have had. Of course, there was one thing that was odd; the man had two suitcases with him and one of them, the larger, was practically empty, as if it had no more than a well-wrapped picture in it. Could it be some work that Mr Blag had been asked to identify? Bristow could be an insurance investigator, a dealer or even some kind of policeman.

'Or a lawyer?' I suggested.

'He could be. Naturally Mr Blag wouldn't want anyone like that in the house.'

But Blag had surprises for everyone that day. Towards six o'clock he came out of his studio, banged on the ironwork of the staircase to bring me out and asked if I fancied a walk to the pub. Jenny was with him, clutching a handkerchief to her breast and looking like Alice Terry on her way to the duel. As I reached the bottom of the stairs she blew a kiss, cried a strangled 'Good luck' and ran back to her own studio. 'Let's go and have a drink with Mr Bristow,' Blag said.

D.J. Bristow was indeed an officer type, but to my mind more navy than army. He had the smooth pink complexion, the

171

tight blue serge suit and the starched collar with the skinny black tie. He was sitting at a table in the rose garden with a glass of beer in front of him and he stood up when he saw us approaching. He and Blag shook hands as if they had met before. I was introduced as one of the London Blagdens. Bristow smiled and nodded. 'Son of Henry? Yes, I thought so.' He turned to Blag. 'Is this young man your photographer?'

'No, Charlie's here to lend moral support. The photographer's waiting inside, all ready to go to work making the copies.'

Bristow pursed his lips. 'Well now. I hope you're not going to be too disappointed, Blag. I was able to bring only one of the pictures. The Town Clerk was very helpful but it was one or none. You see, these photographs are, in a sense, part of the furniture of the council chamber. They are also of some historical significance. Our man held office as a councillor for eighteen years and there are five group photographs with him in them, the last one dated eighteen ninety-five. He was the architect of the Preston town hall annexe completed in that year. I chose that one to bring because it's the sharpest and because he has more facial hair in the earlier ones.'

'I'm sure you did your best.'

'It wasn't easy. I had to promise the Town Clerk that I would have it back in the Town Hall council chamber by Monday morning. And I had to promise that it would not be removed from its frame. It's glazed of course.'

Blag sighed. 'Well, let's go inside and have a look at it.'

Rowe was waiting for us in the oak-panelled dining-room. Jack was in the Morris outside. Bristow went upstairs to get the picture.

'It's framed and glazed,' said Blag, 'and must stay that way. Mr Bristow will not let it out of his sight.'

'I've got a polarizing filter that should take care of the glass,' Rowe said; 'and if the filter doesn't work I'll manage somehow. Is it really valuable?'

'Only to me. You see . . . ' He broke off. Bristow had returned. The picture was wrapped in corrugated paper and tied up with tape from a lawyers' office. The frame inside was about twenty inches by twelve made of ebonized hardwood with gilt beading. A yellowing white mount surrounded the photograph which showed the steps up to the portico of a town hall. Lined up on the steps and standing in two ranks of nine were eighteen gentlemen all formally dressed for the occasion. Some of those in frock coats had mutton-chop whiskers. The rear rank stood two steps above the front so that all were clearly visible. Their names were inscribed in copperplate style in two ranks along the mount below.

'Which is the one we are interested in?' asked Rowe.

Blag reached out and pointed to the second figure from the right in the front row. 'That's the chap,' he said; 'Councillor T.C. Everard. I'd know that face anywhere, wouldn't you? Now let's see if you can blow the good man up. Shall we, Rowe? Eh?'

He was so excited that he could scarcely get the words out. Rowe and Bristow seemed infected too. They bundled the picture back into its wrapping and took it out to the car where Jack was waiting. As they piled into it Blag remembered me and looked back. 'Have a strong drink, Charlie,' he said. 'We'll see you back at the studio.' They drove off.

I didn't want a drink but I wanted badly to talk. It was six thirty on a Saturday, a matinee day then. My mother would be having a sandwich in her dressing-room at the theatre. The Angler's Rest had a phone box in the hall. I had the stage door phone number written in my pocket diary, for emergency use.

When my mother discovered that there was no emergency she was cross but prepared to admit that what I had to report was of interest.

'So, it wasn't the piano tuner she had a romp with, but some sparky young architect from the town hall.'

'It could be.'

'Who did you expect it to be, the Prince of Wales? I say lucky old Blag. He's found the father he always wanted, the one who wasn't a carrier of Huntington's disease. What do you say?'

'I just hope so.'

'What's wrong, Charlie? Speak.'

'I think the Lautrec poster of Bruant looks more like Blag than that man in the photograph, Councillor Everard.'

'Well, let me tell you something, Charlie. Blag once asked his mother why his middle name was Everard. She told him that it had been a mistake, a clerical error by the parish clerk who had bad eyesight. She had wanted his middle name to be Erard after the French piano manufacturers from whom her

173

father had bought her first piano. What's more, the late Mr Cole had served his apprenticeship at Erard's London works. Everard is only an old north-country spelling of the name Edward. Of course she could have been covering up with the wrong spelling story. Are you listening, Charlie?'

'Yes, mother. Mrs Cole would be capable of anything.'

'Yes, but don't you start getting mixed up in Blag's or Jenny's love lives or start taking sides. Come home if you like. We'll manage. But don't start thinking things over and dreaming up stories like your brother. Promise?'

'All right. But Jack says Blag wants to do a portrait of me.'

'I'm sure he'll make you look exactly like your father. Be good, darling.' She hung up.

I did not see Blag again for over a week. Jack said that after Bristow had left with his precious picture Blag and the McGowans had gone up to London, on business. They were staying at Brown's Hotel, all three of them. I knew about Tom McGowan's business. He had been elected a member of the Academy that year and a Bond Street gallery was giving him a show. The picture-framer favoured by the gallery was widely disliked by etchers and engravers for his conceit. The man believed, according to Tom, that a picture frame could have as much as or even more artistic importance than the work it adorned. He looked forward to a hard struggle with the bastard for the integrity of his work. Jenny? Jack thought she would be seeing that publisher of hers, and of course the new films.

The McGowans returned first. Jack met them at the station with the Crossley. They had a festive air about them and that evening at dinner Rowe was bold enough to comment on it. 'You've been shopping for a dress,' he told Jenny; 'I know the look. Is it to be in a church or a registry office?'

Tom McGowan bridled. 'If you know what a special licence cost you'd not be asking such a damn fool question.'

'Then it's to be a registry office, eh?'

I am sure that neither Jack nor Annette uttered a word to anyone, but the idea of a wedding was now abroad at the Farm and the village girl who did Mrs Cole's housework also went in twice a week to the McGowans. Word must have reached Auntie Alice very quickly.

174

I knew when Blag was back because I heard the hire car from Pinner drive away and saw a light in the wall door of the studio. When I went down next morning to make myself tea and toast Jack had a message for me. 'He wants to work. He'd like you to model for him. Gardening togs. Ten o'clock.'

I had been in the walled garden before to do weeding and other odd jobs but I had not seen inside the studio. It was bigger than it looked from the outside. From the inner doorway you saw a deep lofty room with a broad skylight at least thirty feet long, and tall windows with slatted blinds on the garden side. It seemed full of light. There was a tilted drawing table as well as easels and work tables. One of the easels carried a large pin board with drawings and photographs tacked to it. The drawings were mostly sketches of the actor-manager's head and hands and bits of them. The photographs were glossy and more difficult to see from where I stood.

Blag came through a doorway at the other end of the studio. There was a faint smell of cooked kippers. That seemed to be his kitchen with the bed-sitting room beyond.

'Hallo, Charlie,' he said; 'did they get off to the framer's all right?'

'Those boxes of Mr McGowan's wouldn't all go in the Morris.'

'I told Jenny they'd need the big car. Who helped her?'

'Jack and me. Jenny said they'd be back late but not to worry.'

'The framer's in Fulham. They're having dinner with Tom's sister in Chelsea. What do you think of it?'

He had caught my eyes wandering to the biggest photograph pinned to the board. It was the blow-up Rowe had done of the Everard head.

'From that fuzzy old print it's amazing.'

'I expect you're right. Charlie, why don't you try sitting on that bar stool over there. Yes, the one with the arms. Now, lift your head a bit and look out of the window. Head right a bit. What do you see? A flower bed, but what flowers? Geraniums. All right. Relax, but hold still.'

He had a double-demy sheet of cartridge paper pinned to a board on the smaller easel. The easel was on castors. He wheeled it into a position somewhere behind my left shoulder and began to draw. He used charcoal at first then crayon. Then there was a smell of turpentine and he began dabbing at the paper with a sponge. He caught me looking at him and told me to keep still. 'Relax but keep still,' he said. 'I'll tell you when you can move. I'm working in pastel now but I'm using turps as well. You'll look like something by Dégas.'

It was a long time before he spoke again and the cramp in my neck was becoming really painful when there was a hammering at the door to the yard, the one I had come through, and the sound of a woman shouting.

Blag said: 'You can rest for a bit, Charlie, but don't go away. Stay where you are.'

He went to the door and opened it. The noise was coming from Auntie Alice and the golf club she was using as a hammer.

'What on earth are you doing, Alice?'

She pushed past him into the studio. 'The car,' she said. 'That McGowan girl's taken the car. And on my club day. What right has she?'

'I told her to take it. It's a family car. Everyone uses it.'

'The McGowans are not family.'

'They're part of *my* family, Alice,' he said, 'whether you and Mother Autumn like it or not.' He said it very distinctly.

'You're breaking her heart,' Alice sobbed, and then burst into tears. The worst was over. With her grey shingled hair, her tweed skirt and her golfing brogues Alice wasn't dressed for grief, not the persuasive kind. Blag gave her his handkerchief to dry her eyes. 'Jack'll drive you in the Morris,' he said.

'But you'll come and talk to your mother tonight? Blag, you did promise.'

'Oh yes, I promised. Off you go, Alice. Talk to Jack.' He shut the door behind him and returned to the easel. 'All right, Charlie,' he said; 'let's get back to work.'

He worked another hour and then sent me off to lunch. He said that I could have a look at the picture the next day.

I was late for lunch and tired. Annette made me an omelette. After that I went up to my room meaning to read Maitland. Instead I fell asleep. When I woke up I had a bath and changed into my father's Savile Row tweed. Then I walked to the pub, not along the river path because I didn't want Mother Autumn to see me, but along the road. At the pub I met Rowe who had used the road for the same reason as I had. I experimented with a gin and ginger ale.

We were late back for dinner which was Annette's superb rabbit casserole with the white wine and basil sauce. All of us, including the Hunters, drank a lot of wine with it. After dinner they taught me to play nap. It was quite dark when the party broke up. To get some air I went for a walk along the river bank. Then, when it began to drizzle with rain, I quickly walked back.

The studio lights were all on and spilling into the yard. Blag, I thought, would be waiting for Jenny to return home. I was at the top of the spiral staircase when I heard the shot. It was quite a loud bang. I went back down the stairs. As soon as I reached the door I recognized the fired cartridge smell. I called to him. 'Are you there, Blag? Are you all right?' Then I went in.

He was lying on his back at the foot of the easel he had been using that morning and the blood was still pumping from the huge wounds in his chest and neck. The padded end of a mahlstick I had seen him use that morning was clutched in his right hand. In the few seconds I stood looking at that ghastly red bubbling mess my only thought was that the heart must still be beating. So I blundered out into the yard and ran for help.

It took me an age to get it. The Hunters were sound asleep and hard to wake. I knew that Rowe also had a telephone so tried shouting at him to call a doctor. The noise I made brought Jack downstairs with a raincoat over his pyjamas. I did *not* say 'Blag's shot himself.' I said, 'Blag's been shot.' Jack said, 'Dear God Almighty' and ran to the studio door. As I followed him I was chattering about getting a doctor.

Minutes must have elapsed between my finding Blag wounded and re-entering the studio with Jack. The second time was quite different. I could not stand where I had stood before. There was the family shot-gun lying on the floor just where I had stood.

Jack was crouched over the mess on the floor. He glanced up at me sharply. 'If you're going to puke, Charlie,' he said, 'you'd best do it outside. It's not the local doctor we'll be needing but the police surgeon.'

Blag had thrown a cloth over the portrait on the easel. Now Jack pulled it off to cover the dead man's face. That left my face looking at me from the easel. As Jack had suggested I should, I went outside to be sick.

I was still doing so when the lights of the returning Crossley swept into the stable yard of Elm Park Farm. Jenny had returned. The bad dream entered its horror phase.

The coroner's inquest was at Isleworth near the hospital at which the autopsy had been performed. The courtroom was a territorial drill hall with not enough seating to accommodate the press. The place was packed.

The Coroner was a local medical officer of health with some forensic qualifications. I was among the first to give evidence. I told the court about hearing the shot, about finding Blag wounded and about running for help to the Hunters.

'That is Mr Jack Hunter who called the police?'

'Yes, sir. There was nothing I could have done for those wounds, but Jack had been in the war.'

'Thank you, Mr Blagden. I'm sure you did all you could. You saw Mr Cole that morning. How would you describe his state of mind?'

'Impatient, sir. He wanted no interruptions of his work or of his life.'

That was the end of me. Jack Hunter came next. The star turn, however, was Dr Lionel Benton-Black who had an address in Harley Street and who was consultant neurologist at a London teaching hospital. Blag Cole had been a patient of his for nearly twenty years.

'Suffering from what disease, Doctor?'

'I don't know for certain, sir, and now I never shall. His sister had died of Hereditary Progressive Chorea when he was referred to me. That is the disease of the central nervous system which is now generally known as Huntington's disease. The disease is hereditary and genetically transmitted through either parent or both. There is at present no blood or other body fluid test that can detect its presence. There are Huntington families – I know too many of them – and they are in a sense doomed. If the disease is there genetically, it can always strike, most commonly in the third, fourth, fifth and sixth decades of a person's life. There are family histories of Huntington's going back ten generations. It has been described as the most vicious of hereditary diseases. Vicious is not a scientific term but I can understand its use in this context.'

'When did you last see the deceased?'

TO BE CONTINUED

'Three weeks ago. He said he had firm evidence to show that his father, the proved Huntington's carrier in that family, had not been his natural father. He claimed that he had been conceived illegitimately before his mother's marriage to Mr Cole. He could not, he argued, be a Huntington's carrier. There was no reason, therefore, why he could not marry and beget children.'

'Did you believe him, Doctor?'

'He had a good case, and photographs and other documents to support it. Probably all fantasy. With those who reach middle age it often happens. They have fantasies. Then they commit suicide. With men that is the most common outcome. I told Blagden Cole that on the subject of marriage he must use his own judgement.'

The verdict, of course, was suicide, 'while the balance of his mind was disturbed.'

On the way out I felt a tap on my shoulder.

'Hello, young man.' It was Mr Bristow. 'You look as if you could do with a beer.'

I was glad to see him. I needed someone to share my awful secret. When I told him about the shot-gun that wasn't there when I found Blag but *was* there when I returned with Jack Hunter he nodded approvingly. 'Not suicide, you think, but murder. What did the police think of the idea?'

'They were patient and kind. Naturally, when I found Blag with those terrible injuries I would be in a state of shock. It was quite understandable that I hadn't noticed the gun first time.'

'And it was understandable.'

'It was also understandable that Blag would hold the mahlstick by the wrong end. The police say that he used the stick to press the shot-gun trigger and kill himself.'

'And you don't?'

'I think that when he saw the gun pointing straight at him he grabbed the stick to try to deflect the gun barrel. He almost succeeded. The wounds were mainly on the right side.'

He sipped his beer. 'And who pointed the gun? Mother Autumn?'

'Blag went to see her that evening to confront her with that picture of Councillor Everard that you found for him and to announce his marriage. When he left she took the gun, which

179

was kept with Alice's golf clubs, and followed him. She shot him. Then, still holding the gun she walked back to her own house. On the way she met Alice who had heard the shot. It was Alice who took the gun from her and left it on the studio floor for us to find.

'You'll never prove any of that, young man.'

'I won't be trying, Mr Bristow.'

He had been fumbling in his brief-case. Now he pulled out a print of the Councillor Everard blow-up. 'You may like this as a souvenir,' he said. 'The case for Everard as Blag's natural father is about as sound as the verdict of suicide to which we have just listened. Everard married twice but had no children. His fault, probably. As a young man he had a commission in the Yeomanry and, in the year before Blag was born, attended an Officers' Ball at Preston barracks at which Miss Emma Blagden was also present. That is recorded in a local newspaper of the time. I say no more. Good luck with the law, young man. I have a train to catch at Euston.'

When I got home I showed the photograph to my mother.

'That one never fathered Blag,' she said. 'Nothing like him. Wrong bones. The only good portrait I've ever seen of Blag was the one he did of his mother. I mean the nasty one he wrote on the back of, the one he said was of Ibsen's Mrs Alving.'

It was over twenty years before the subject of Blagden Cole came up again between us. In the mid-fifties a play of mine was opening in New York and she came over to see it. Of course, she had pieces of gossip.

'Do you remember that girl Jenny, the one Blag Cole was going to marry? Well, after the suicide I kept in touch with her. Blag had got her pregnant you know. Well, you wouldn't know. You were away.'

'What happened?'

'She had a daughter. Nice child. Died in her twenties, poor thing.'

'Huntington's?'

'Yes, I thought you'd be interested. My new doctor says they think now that in ten or twelve years' time they may be able to tell if someone's a carrier. Gene-mapping they call it. Yes, Jenny herself is all right. Children's book illustrating. I have to admit, though, I always found her a teeny bit silly.' She was silent for a moment and then sighed. 'Of course one has to be fair. You thought that mother of his shot him, and perhaps you were right. But the one who really did for poor old Blag was the piano tuner.'